does your mama know?

does your mama know?

An
Anthology
of Black Lesbian
Coming Out Stories

Edited by

Lisa C. Moore

RedBone Press
Austin, TX

does your mama know? An Anthology of Black Lesbian Coming Out Stories

Published by:

RedBone Press

P.O. Box 1805

Austin, Texas 78767

97 98 99 00 01   10 9 8 7 6 5 4 3

Second edition, third printing

Illustration and design by Kamela Eaton © 1996

Logo design by Mignon Goode

Permissions acknowledgements appear on pp. 309-313

Printed in the United States of America

ISBN 0-9656659-0-9 $19.95

"I love the name of your imprint & am impressed by your work & vision. 'YOU GO, GIRL!!' "

Take Care, Woman!
— Terri Jewell
May 30, 1995

In memory of Terri Jewell, who lit a fire in my heart and under my butt and kept me going.

Acknowledgements

I would like to thank, first and foremost, the contributors, without whom this book would not be in your hands now. Their work has made my work possible.

Thanks to my sister Eleanor, who gave me the instantly recognizable title; my sister Lylah, who gave me typing time and bookstore know-how; my sister Shahidah, who watched and waited; my brother Keith, for his subtle pride; and future brother-in-law Jason Lockridge, who gave his artist's eye.

Praise be to Kamela Eaton, who endured my indecision and produced a gorgeous cover; Mignon Goode, who designed a fabulous logo; and to Valerie Boyd, editor extraordinaire, who led me to them both.

My heartfelt appreciation goes to Barbara Smith and Makeda Silvera for their encouragement.

Also, thanks to Michelle Wilkinson, for her unending support; Imani Henry, for her incredible faith in me and passion for this work; Liz Messerly, who kept things from getting too crazy; Denise Moore, for providing insight and feedback on politics vs. ethics; Imar Hutchins, for welcoming me as a "gristler"; Curtis Parker, for his gracious emergency layout expertise; and Michele Riley, for recess and reality check.

And my ultimate (in all meanings of the word) thanks to my father, John E. Moore; mother, Janet Salahuddin; and aunt, Sybil Kein. Your encouragement has meant more than you'll ever know.

Introduction
by Lisa C. Moore

Imagine you're going about your daily life — getting the kids ready for school, washing the breakfast dishes, taking something out to thaw. Going out into the world every day, coming home to get dinner ready, feed the kids, help with homework, do a couple of loads of laundry. By the time bedtime rolls around, you're exhausted. Just another day in a black woman's life.

But one day something happens. Some hint, some spark of recognition. It could be in a book, a passing conversation, a look from a stranger — but it ultimately changes your life.

So it happened with me. I was 13 years old when I realized I was gay.

By the time I was 12, I had been running the household for some time. My parents divorced when I was very young, my mother remarried a few years later, and subsequently gave birth to my three sisters within four years. In order for my mother to work to make ends meet, I took over childcare and housework. At the time, I didn't question the situation; that's just the way things were.

I didn't question a lot when it came to emotions. At 12, I got my period, but I'd already read up on it, so I was prepared. I don't even remember being scared. And sex was the furthest thing from my mind. I had too much work to do.

Actually, my mother realized I was a lesbian first, and told my father, who told me. I had never heard the word before. My dad came to my high school to take me out to lunch. As we walked to Burger King, he said, "Your mother seems to think you're a lesbian." Cautious child that I was, I hedged. "Nah, I don't think so," I said, making a mental note to look that word up. "Oh," he said. And that was it. He didn't mention it again — well, not for at least 15 years or so.

Right after lunch, I tore up the steps to the school library to look up the "L" word. Hell, I wasn't going to let on to anybody that I didn't know the meaning of a word, not even my dad, who I'm incredibly close to. Once I found the definition, I felt like I'd known it all along. That was the feeling I'd been having for my

i

algebra tutor, the one I called at night just to talk.

Since that lunch with my dad, I've come out in so many ways, it's not even funny. Not only to myself, but to my friends (and lost some of them to ignorance), my parents (one at a time, and what a long strange trip that was!), my siblings and select co-workers at various jobs. But that first conversation with my dad was my first realization I was gay.

Five years ago, at 28, I moved to Atlanta, hoping to find a friendly out black lesbian community. I'd been living in Connecticut for three years, but my job forced me to travel 85 percent of the time, so what friends I had were the long-distance-phone-call kind. I reasoned that if Atlanta was 60 percent black, surely 10 percent of that would be gay. And with a population of 3 million... you do the math!

But when I got here, I found that things were different from Hartford, or New Orleans, or any other city I'd lived. I saw many young black women riding MARTA (Atlanta's rapid transit system) passing for boys: breasts bound, cigarettes in shirt pockets, pants hanging off their butts b-boy style, with another young woman on their arm. It blew my mind!

You see, I came out in college in a community of white lesbians. In the early 1980s, coming out literature was all the rage, and I'd read it all. So had everybody I knew. I felt sure of my sexuality, and the support of my friends and some of my family meant I didn't feel like I was "funny," "wanted to be a man," or "really needed a good dick." Sure, I looked for black images in gay literature, but the lack of them didn't phase me much because I'd always gone to white schools and all my friends were white. I was used to it. After moving to Atlanta, though, I found myself completely surrounded by beautiful black women; it altered my perception of reality. Black folk are the majority here. Suddenly, I longed for black images in gay literature; I found it incredibly lacking.

Black women have a rich oral history of lesbianism: Everybody knows of the bulldagger up the block that their mamas used to talk about. Of the auntie the family used to dog. Of the rumors about the basketball player at college. And when black women talk at get-togethers, the coming out stories fly! "What was your first girlfriend like? When did you know you were in the life? Did you think you were the only one? Do you remember the first girl you kissed? The first girl who kissed you?"

But I realized that these stories weren't written; there was nothing that a young black lesbian — riding the train, passing for boy with a good-looking woman on her arm — could go to for reference, to know that she's not the only one. That she has stories of bulldaggers and he-she's and femmes and butches and old maid aunties. Old ones and young ones. And that we are here, we've always been here, and look how glorious it all is!

So, I believed this book was necessary. I think that by making these stories available, black lesbians will become aware of their history, and feel comfort and strength from that knowledge. I know I always did whenever I walked away from those get-togethers.

* * * * *

This collection of coming out stories is unique for many reasons, the primary one being that all of the voices within these pages are black. There are African-Americans, biracial women, Jamaican-Canadians, Haitian-Americans, Louisiana creoles, Jamericans ... and even one white lesbian, whose telling of a young black woman's first crush was so well-written, I called the author to ask for permission to reprint it, and she said, "You know I'm white, right?" But the literary voice was black, and that voice had helped me in another aspect of *my* coming out. I believe that if the story can help another young black woman come to terms with her sexuality, then it is worth reprinting.

You will find the no-regrets tale of a 90-year-old (and count-ing) African-American woman in Terri Jewell's interview of "Miss Ruth." In "Be Still and Know," a woman comes to terms with God and her sexuality. Caribbean girlhood is explored within Makeda Silvera's "Man Royals and Sodomites." Tonia Bryan, a fierce writer living in Canada, questions the rigid definition of a lesbian. Cheryl Clarke and Eva Yaa Asantewaa illustrate that yes, married women can be lesbians, too.

But there's more. The first few lines of Terri Jewell's "A Short

Account of My Behavior" produces an eerie feeling, as well as a feeling of sadness, now that's she's gone. Michele Hunter's "Coming Out Story" reflects biracial realities heretofore unexplored in much of popular literature. Sheree Slaughter wrote "And Now They Know" when she was 14; the poem portrays a sense of teenage longing for acceptance.

These coming out stories run the gamut, from young lesbians to old, single and married, this country and that one — and they retell the joy of coming out to yourself, the uncertainty of coming out to your teacher, the anger at finding out sometimes your mama would rather not know you.

These women have gone out on a limb to share their voices, coming out in a most public way. It is my hope that this book will get black people talking, and remembering that we are yet another layer of richness in the black community. I also hope that this book will be a starting point for black women who are just coming out and need to know that we're out here.

We *are* out here. I only wish you could have heard us sooner.

Contents

2

1985: Memories of My Coming Out Year
by Hope Massiah

I spent 1985 coming out. It took the whole year, and it all started
with Kat. I remember the exact moment that I knew I loved her:

Spring

Kat and I are walking in the South Downs hills on a bright
spring morning. Kat is walking briskly, I walk more slowly,
trying to identify wildflowers. We come to a clearing in the
woods and stand admiring the hills rolling all the way down to
the coast. As we stand there, a wave of joy sweeps over me; my
chest hurts, I feel breathless. It is a lovely view, but I know that
the feeling is about Kat, about being with her. I am overjoyed; it
is pure feeling, not a thought I can dissect, unravel or analyze. I
realize that I love Kat more than a friend, but I accept it; how
could I not, how could I be anything but glad to experience such
joy?

Kat is my best friend. I met her on my first day as math
teacher at a south London high school. She is the new history
teacher, fresh out of college, just like me. Unlike me — crisp
pleated skirt, crepe blouse, small sensible heels — she looks very
scruffy, but I am drawn to her confidence, confidence to have
hair that short, to wear trousers and an old cardigan on her first
day at Furzedown, which considers itself to be one of the better
state schools.

A month later I see her in Brixton market and I realize that
she dresses up for work. She is wearing a long faded floral dress
and plimsolls.* We talk and agree to meet up the next weekend
at the Marxism Today Conference. I meet Kat's friends at the
conference and I am not impressed; the women dress like her in
old dresses and plimsolls; the men wear old jeans, donkey

---

* plimsolls — gym shoes

jackets, monkey boots* and NHS glasses.*

But gradually Kat and I become friends. She is an enthusiastic teacher who encourages her kids to look at history from the perspective of ordinary people, not just kings and politicians. I tell her about the anti-racist teaching materials I've been developing, and we do a joint math and history project with our second years (7th grade) on Hypatia, an Egyptian mathematician.

As we grow closer, we start to see our common family histories of large families, mothers both nurses, religious upbringing: hers Catholic, mine Seventh-day Adventist, but there the similarities ended — though her family are not wealthy, there are thoroughly upper middle classed. Kat is public school-* and Cambridge-educated, a world away from me. Her friends are either cheerfully unemployed — going to India, learning juggling and clowning — or landing jobs as actors, directors and producers. Her world is strange, yet familiar; the world of white people in books, films and television; the world I grew up dreaming about.

I am the product of a working class Black family and Black church community, attended state schools and an undistinguished university. I love my family but by comparison they, we, seem dull, unremarkable, our lives too commonplace to document. I see myself as terminally ordinary, not the sort of person who inspires great love. Yet slowly I start to see that my regard for Kat isn't one-sided; she asks my opinion, repeats my ideas to others, starts to use a few of my phrases. We talk so much that we develop shared views on feminism, capitalism and nuclear disarmament.

Not long after that day on the South Downs, Kat rings me: Tom, her boyfriend, is graduating from Cambridge and has asked

---

* jackets, monkey boots — cheap hardwearing workman's jacket and boots

* NHS glasses — A limited range of glasses heavily subsidized by the National Health Service and therefore very cheap.

* Public school — the most exclusive private boarding schools

her to go down. We had planned to see each other. She says, "If you want to go, we'll both go; otherwise we won't." So we hitch to Cambridge. Then just before Easter, Tom says to me, "So is Kat going to Greenham with you or to Brighton with me?" He is lighthearted, I am lighthearted. Does he see me as a threat? By now I don't feel threatened by Tom or any of her other friends. I know she will want to be with me.

We hitch down to Greenham Common Women's Peace Camp for the first time at Easter. I am carefully dressed in saggy leggings and a thick jumper, and my things are proudly packed in my army surplus rucksack that I bought in Brixton market for a fiver.

At Greenham, the women are camped at the seven gates of the camp, which they have named after the colors of the rainbow. When we arrive at Green gate, the first woman we meet asks if it is our first time. When we excitedly reply "Yes," she snaps, "Why did it take you so long to come!" The women who live there look scornfully at our shop-bought tent. They are constantly being evicted by the police, so they live in benders: homemade shelters of clear plastic, blankets and branches.

Summer

Kat and I develop a passionate friendship, complete with late-night conversations, rows and reconciliations. Everyone thinks we are lovers: our friends, other teachers, even the kids start to suspect something. We are filled with righteous indignation: "Just because two women choose to prioritize their friendship everyone thinks they're lesbians," and we continue fighting giggles in school assembly, wearing each other's clothes and leaving school together every day.

I spend most of the summer holidays at Greenham. I live at Turquoise, a new camp in the woods between Green and Blue gates. I get used to heavy boots which cause blisters but keep the rain out, smelling like a kipper* from sitting around the wood

---

* Kipper — a smoked fish, usually eaten for breakfast

fire, using the shit pit, having to walk three miles into town to take a shower and being shouted at by the locals who seem to prefer the nuclear weapons to us: One writes in the local paper "at least Cruise [nuclear missile] is clean."

We are committed to getting nuclear weapons off the base and out of the country, so we cut through the perimeter fence and get into the base at every opportunity. We are prepared to get arrested; it gives us a chance to make speeches in the courtroom about the link between nuclear weapons, the military-industrial complex and violence against women. As there are so many of us, we are sentenced to a day in prison and we emerge feeling heroic, ready to do it all over again.

Before an action, we stand in a circle, arms linked, drawing strength from each other. They are my sisters. For the first time since leaving church, I have a sense of belonging, of communion, the shared sense of purpose I have been looking for.

As it gets hotter, women start dyeing their hair blonde, changing their names to Autumn, Oak and Leaf; start talking about sex, monogamy and political lesbianism; running workshops on "The Seduction of Women and Related Matters."

A bunch of us walk back to Turquoise, going home after a workshop at Green gate. We sing "A Woman Needs a Man Like a Fish Needs a Bike." I feel like a fraud when we get to the line, "But loving is better than fucking and its great to be a dyke." I love Kat and I'm starting to have crushes on women here, but I am still straight, still on the pill. Except I keep forgetting to take it and I get breakthrough bleeding. The woman I borrow pads from says, "Yeah, we're being zapped by electromagnetic waves from the base. It's fucking up a lot of women's cycles." I agree, afraid to tell her the truth.

One beautiful golden morning Kat appears in the woods in a white vest, khaki shorts and big boots, looking golden from her fortnight in Turkey with Tom; but she has come to spend the rest of the summer with me. I run to her, we run to each other, hold each other tight. I know something else then, that I am falling in love with her.

My dreams are full of Kat. I can't stop watching her, the way

8

she strides around collecting firewood; the way she pulls her leather belt tight on her old khaki shorts; the way she holds up her large hand like a cup and swivels her wrist as she talks. Her nose, such a big nose; amazing the way it starts at her eyes and goes all the way down past her nostrils, like a ski run. No bigger than other white people's noses, but enormous to me. The way she manages to exude perfect health while getting out her tin of Golden Virginia and rolling cigarette after cigarette.

I eat a white peach for the first time, and as I examine the color of the freshly-bitten flesh, pale but warm, I think of Kat. I am intoxicated by her, but I feel uncomfortable about the fact that I am supposed to be, that the world recognizes her tall, blonde, good looks but has nothing to say about mine.

I am the only Black woman at Greenham, and I grow tired of the repeated refrain, "Why don't more Black women come to Greenham?" I ask what they are doing to reach out to Black women. They look puzzled. I suggest they contact Black women's groups. They don't know of any. How about having a Black women-only gate? They look totally confused: "But why; we are all women." Eventually I draw away; I realize that they don't want me to tell them what they could do. They want me, a Black woman, to tell them that there is some quirk in Black women that stops them/us from wanting to get involved in The Struggle.

My sister is getting married, so I come back from Greenham to be chief bridesmaid. I've wanted to be a bridesmaid ever since I was little and feminism hasn't changed that. I am still excited about wearing a nice dress, sitting at the top table and being fed first. All the other bridesmaids wear size 8 calf-length salmon pink dresses and have flowers in their hair. I wear the same dress, except mine is long, fuschia pink and size 14. I don't want to wear flowers, so I dye my Grace Jones flat-top fuschia pink to match my dress.

It's my first time going back to church since I left two years ago, and I brace myself for the tears, the "When are you coming back to church?" and the "It'll be your turn next."

Beverley's wedding completes the severing process that started when I went away to college and was accelerated by my

9

leaving church. When we were younger, I was the silent little sister who tagged along. Her jet black plaits stayed straight, as if they had lead weights attached to the bottom. My rust-colored plaits shrunk up until they rested around my ears like worms. Her afro was round, mine was square.

Although I am starting to see matrimony as a patriarchal plot, a small part of me envies my sister. She is living the life I was brought up to live. I miss the certainty of being a Seventh-day Adventist: knowing how the world started, how it's going to end, the meaning of everything. Trying to make sense of the world on my own feels like staring into an abyss: What is good or bad? Does it matter? What is the point of my life, of life itself? The enormity of these questions is almost enough to drive me back to the safety of the church, so I keep them well to the back of my mind.

Autumn

It's a new school year. I am no longer a probationary teacher and I have my own tutor group of bright, well-behaved first years (6th grade). Most of the male teachers, including the ones that flirted with me at last year's Christmas party, don't talk to me anymore. I am no longer a sweet young teacher; my hair is too short, I am a man-hating feminist, or worse.

Autumn at Greenham: It's unusually hot and women are getting off with each other everywhere. No one is talking about the struggle or the base, there are no actions being planned; women are languid, flirting, touching. One pair spend the days lying naked, snogging.* I want to watch, but I don't want to watch. The whole gate is infected with their sexual energy. Am I just being swept along by everyone else's desire? I've been falling in love with one little boy after another since I was 5 years old, but now that I am in a lesbian environment I am attracted to women. Thinking about Kat all the time.

---

* Snogging — Petting, necking

Another weekend at Greenham: Sitting around the fire on a cool evening; someone is reading *Alice in Wonderland* aloud. I'm enjoying the dark, the stillness, the warmth of the fire and the fantastical story. Cuddling with Kat, feeling more and more in love with her. I want her so much I am frightened; but we haven't talked about it.

We are camped next to a couple who do it all the time, loudly. Kat and I sit in our tent, conversation halted by loud gasps and shudders. We wait quietly until she comes; it seems impolite to continue talking. When they finish, we resume our conversation.

I keep seeing a poster for Peckham Black Lesbian Group when I go to WAVAW (Women Against Violence Against Women) meetings. I want to go, but I can't go to a group with "lesbian" in the title. I am a stalwart of WAVAW, a regular at Greenham, I go to lots of women-only events where 99.99% of the women are lesbians, but they are events for all women. Everyone assumes I am a lesbian, but no one has ever asked me straight out.

Occasionally I see a Black woman, a shadowy figure rolling a joint or knocking back a Red Stripe* in the gloom at the back of a women-only club. They always look hard and never return my tentative smiles. I am sure Peckham Black Lesbian Group would be made up of these women and I can't imagine what we would find to talk about, except racism. Even the thought of walking into a room full of them terrifies me. I'm sure they would see past my lesbian façade very quickly.

For Halloween, Kat and I go to Lorraine's party. Lorraine greets us at the door carrying a brush broom. She is wearing a homemade white satin witch's dress, and her shaved-with-long-bits bleached blonde hair is full of jelly snakes. We are a bit afraid of Lorraine: She is a leading light in WAVAW and a revolutionary and radical lesbian feminist. Kat and I have our first proper slow dance to "Move Closer" by Phyllis Nelson.

---

* Red Stripe — a strong Jamaican beer

"When we're together, touching each other,
and our bodies do what we feel."
It feels good to hold her, to finally have a reason to press
against her. We get to the chorus:
"Move closer,
move your body real close until we
feel like we're really making love."
Other women are singing along, but I can hardly breathe.
Every breath has become a gasp, every swallow a gulp. She must
hear it.
My longing for her is becoming unbearable, but we don't talk
about it. We do everything together, talk about everything else. I
know she loves me, but does she feel like I feel?

I am starting to move in a lesbian world and feel like I am a
lesbian, but what does this white lesbian world have to do with
me? Inside I am still Hope, one of the Massiahs, up until a few
years ago a good, clean-living church girl.
My family still haven't recovered from me leaving church.
They took it in shocked silence. I know they are heartbroken at
the prospect of me going to hell. I don't have any explanations
for them, so I don't try to talk about it either. My communica-
tions have become very superficial, even with my sister, who
used to be the closest person in the world to me. I miss being one
of them. I miss:
"You Massiahs all have that smile."
"Wait, is this Beverley or Hope?"
"Carmen mus' 'e jus' spit you out!"
My mum took it quietly until the first time she saw me
wearing lipstick. She cried and shouted at me, but I think now
she wishes I would wear lipstick. She looks pained at my short
hair, boots and secondhand men's jackets. She notices people
staring at me, calling me "Sir" when we are buying fish in
Brixton market. I know she is praying for me.
My oldest brother Phil is worried about me going to
Greenham. He is afraid I will be led astray by a strange white
woman in a checked shirt. Only in my dreams, Phil.

When I left church, I left my community behind me. This left

12

my college and teaching friends, who were pretty much all white. For the first time in my life I have to go out to try to meet Black people. I went to Brixton Anti Apartheid and CND (Campaign for Nuclear Disarmament): All white. At Brixton Black Women's Centre, I found one dispirited woman who reminisced about the good old days of OWAAD (Organization of Women of African and Asian Descent), but had nothing to tell me about events happening now for Black women.

Winter

I feel like I am carrying my sexuality around my neck and it is getting larger and heavier. I can't wake or go to sleep without thinking about it. I remind myself of that old spiritual:
"Have mercy on me oh Lord for I am undone,
I am wretched and most miserable.
When night comes I long for the day,
And when the day breaks I long for the night again."
    Yup, that sums me up.
    I can't talk to anyone about it and I retreat, as I always do in times of stress, into the world of books. I may not have any Black friends in the real world, but I have plenty here: Toni Cade Bambara, Alice Walker, Rosa Guy, Paule Marshall and Toni Morrison. I've bought a book called *Zami* that's supposed to be about Black lesbians, but I can't get into it.

After months of growing sexual tension, I finally break down and tell Kat that I fancy her. I am stoned for the first time and out of control, like a sloppy drunk. Kat is very cool, she waits until I finish, then says, "I did fancy you for a while, but I got over it." She makes it sound like she'd had a cold, like I should ask her if she's fully recovered now. She then confides that she fancies her friend Rachel. Rachel, like most of Kat's college friends, is a tall, androgynous pre-Raphaelite beauty. Someone else I can never match up to. Rachel thinks the world of Kat, though she is straight. I had to retire to bed crying for the rest of the weekend.

Winter at Greenham: It's really cold, -5 degrees Celsius. It's too cold to do anything but sit around the fire or get into a

13

sleeping bag, so I doze in the Cathedral bender in my four-season "mummy" sleeping bag. I wake up to the sound of glass breaking; I look up and see ice crystals forming and breaking on the clear plastic of the bender. I have a wonderful view of the trees and the sky, but to be covered by only a sheet of plastic seems like madness. I pack up my things and go to the Hidden bender where Kat is staying. It is covered in branches and twigs and brush and can only be seen from its small entrance. Things have settled down between us, but we are still treating each other very gently. I am afraid that we have lost the easy, unspoken closeness that we had, maybe forever. We are supposed to be staying in separate benders for the first time, to give each other space, but Kat welcomes me into the dark, warm cave. We kiss goodnight and we fall asleep in each other's arms, under a mountain of blankets.

We spend the days sitting around the fire eating chocolate and oranges, left over from Christmas. It's too cold to get enough wood to cook, too cold to walk into town to buy groceries. Fortunately, some supporters have organized a minibus which delivers hot meals every night. We are the last gate to be fed, and by the time our food arrives it is lukewarm and we are cold, ungrateful and stuffed full of chocolate.

The shit pit is visible from the fire and when anyone uses it, the women around the fire watch and comment on their performance. It's a bit of a dis-incentive to using it. Also, if you leave the fire the person sitting in the direction of the smoke takes your place, and when you come back you have to sit in the smoke, coughing and spluttering. Sisterhood has died of exposure.

New Year's Eve: I left Greenham early because I had the most dreadful stomach cramps. I was really worried, but now I realize that I didn't use the shit pit once while I was there. A flushing toilet with a door, and suddenly I feel a lot better. I turn the heating up, pull a quilt over me and try again with *Zami*.

I read *Zami* in one sitting, and by the end I have found a new friend and big sister. I feel Audre Lorde saying to me: It's okay to still feel Barbadian, to be interested in politics, to struggle with ideas, to try to make sense of the world, to miss my family, to miss church, to want to live a different way, to love women, even

14

white women.

Zami also shows me that somewhere there is a world of Black women: frying fish, getting dressed up, having parties, falling in love. Black women with Black women, not just taking a quick respite from racism, but living their lives.

I realize that a big part of what is holding me back was the feeling that if I become a lesbian, I would have to live in a white world. Black women are welcome, but it was still a white world. I enjoy visiting this world, but after five years of college and teaching I am ready to go home. Home, where I am not Black, I am Hope. I can't go back to the home that I grew up in, the world of my family and church — I don't belong there anymore. I have to find a new home.

When I read *Zami* I know that home for me as a Black lesbian exists, and I know it is only a matter of time until I find it.

Kat rings from Greenham; she walked into town to call. We exchange "I love you's" and "Happy New Year's." They are celebrating the new year by spray-painting the base. I am going to Lorraine's New Year's Eve party. I have made my New Year's resolutions for 1986. They are:

(i) to watch less TV

(ii) to be less of a consumer and make more things myself

(iii) to read more

(iv) to write in my diary every day

(v) to go to Peckham Black Lesbian Group.

A Letter for Life
by Arlene Williams

this letter,   poem.....
is to explain how I feel, who I am.....
how poetic my life has been,
we haven't really talked,
about my life,
about me,
just about,
I love you mom with all of my being,
that is nothing I have to prove to you,
it's about me,
sick, no I'm not sick,
a little cough now and then,
not sick,
Bob— he's ok I guess,
I haven't seen him lately,
no we were never dating,
sick mom,
I'm not sick,
anyway,
we should really talk,
about me,
listen,

I hold strong feelings
the passion of life in love
I reached out toward the flower
to touch the petals of a womyn
and the nectar of a sweet
bitter scent _ _ _ _.

a womyn,
a love not rare, but intense,
strong,
beautiful,
poetic,

17

the poetry I live,
God —
yes God,
I know,
he will save me,
from what,
love.... poetry.... passion,
what's his name,
who do I love,
this is no joke,
his name is
womyn,
she is who I love,
womyn,
mom I love wimmin,
there that's it,
wimmin the issue is wimmin,
beautiful Black wimmin,
beautiful wimmin,
beautiful wimmin of colour,
and I love them all,
Don't cry,
don't cry mom,
Pray
you want me to pray,
pray for what,
for me not to love,
not to love wimmin,
or not to be loved,
loved by you,
love that only you,
mom, mom, --------mommy
and soon I will be loved,
by you,
again but now,
I will,
I will pray,
for me

18

and
for you,
love you always

your daughter
Arlene

A Path to Wholeness
by Martine C. Barbier

I was looking at the student activities bulletin board at school, and trying to absorb the information as inconspicuously as I could without being too obvious.

... Stonewall Coalition Meeting...Lesbian Orientation at The Center on Wednesday...

I passed by that posting quite often, but could never stand in front of it for long. "What time did it say, 2:30 or 3? Damn, I forgot to check, what was the room number again?"

What if someone saw me, or called out a name? Luckily for me, the posting was right beside a flier for the Black Student Union's fashion show. My race is pretty obvious, but could they tell about my sexual orientation? Could they tell from the way my eyes contoured up and down the bodies of the fine women who crowded the bathroom mirrors in the morning? Did they speculate when I did my oral report in speech class on the evolution of black women writers since Phyllis Wheatley and paid strong tribute to my favorites, Audre Lorde and Jewelle Gomez? Did they listen? Did they care? Well if they didn't, I sure did.

I've been waiting seven years. SEVEN years of pretending. In the Book of Revelations, it says that seven is the number which is the symbol of perfection. What have I perfected? Maybe it was the skill of being in the closet and feigning my interests for men. Being closeted is an ornate mental chore that I feel I have mastered so well I should be close to getting a Ph.D. already. But the reality of it all is that I've spent every moment of those years alone in the claustrophobic conscience of my mind. Eventually my secret began to fester inside of me, and suddenly I found myself coming out in different ways.

Hanging posters of male "hunks" on the walls of my dorm room and hiding the hunkettes under my bed inside an empty Kotex box was not helping. Oh sure, those guys were cute, but they never entered my dreams at night. As a child I always did prefer the Tooth Fairy to Mr. Sandman, if you know what I mean.

But now I'm 20 years old and only getting older. It is during these 20-something years that one is supposed to break into the mature world of responsibilities and obligations. My college experiences for the past three years have given me those chances: I've maintained my scholarship, served in jury duty last winter break, voted in the past elections, paid my taxes on time.

Now I've finally decided to touch base with another important part of my inalienable rights — the pursuit of happiness. I have the life and liberty parts pretty much embellished, but my personal life's happiness depends also on my liberty to be the noble bulldagger that I was intended to be. I wanted my last year in college to end with the truth. It was to be my coming out year.

* * * * *

I remember in high school how I pretended to revel in the excitement of my friends as they would recount bit by bit every minute of their dates and the various guys they slept with. I was 13 years old when I entered my womanhood. My personal account is not the de-flowering type that the straight girls wanted to hear or could possibly conceptualize. I am talking about the discovery of the self. It was a discovery that led to the path of my wholeness.

It all began in the summer before ninth grade when I was getting over the first crush I ever had developed for a woman — my history teacher, Ms. Simms. Rather than staying home trying to convince myself that "maybe it's just a phase," I went to a party that my sister Sasha was invited to one evening.

"Is this one of those boring get-togethers on Haitian politics again?" I inquired.

"*Mwen pa konnen*. I don't know," she stated in her usual dialect of French, Creole and English. "My friend Erika is hosting it. She said it will be a mixture of different types of Caribbean music. It's gonna be lots of fun; don't be so fussy."

"I was just checking. I'll wear the cream pantsuit you handed down to me," I said. "So when should I expect you? Mommy says don't be too late."

"Tell *Manman* not to worry, I'll be there as soon as Marc finds

22

the invitation, OK? *Tout de suite.* Besides, I hear you've been kinda gloomy lately, what's wrong? *Ki sa w genyen Marie Claire?"*

"Nothing is wrong with me, Sasha. I miss you, that's all."

My sister and I are ten years apart in age and rarely go out together. I missed our special times; ever since she got married and moved to Brooklyn with her husband Marc, things haven't been the same. She practically raised me, since mother was always working as the housekeeper for the Cottinghams by day, and taking care of their children by night. They gave us the bottom portion of their two-family home in exchange for her baby-sitting their children six days a week. Sasha had already taken on the role of "mother's helper" at an early age, especially since our father's alleged disappearance by the Tonton Macoutes during the "Baby Doc" or Jean-Claude Duvalier regime, when he was accused of being a member of an oppositional party. I never knew my father, but I was told that he was the type who relentlessly stood for his beliefs.

Immigrating from Haiti's small southern town of Petite Riviere de Nip to New York was only the first step in a long road of strife for my mother, who, upon arriving in the U.S., discovered she was pregnant with my brother Fabien; thus Sasha was quickly engaged in the role of motherhood. I was 11 when she left our house in Rockland County, and I often blamed Marc for taking her away. Now I realize that she's never been happier in her entire life. I guess she felt liberated from having to take care of us younger ones throughout her teen and pre-adult years. I figured maybe it's the reason why she hasn't borne any children yet at age 30.

* * * * *

The mid-July humidity weighed heavily over the streets like the dull pain that ceased to evaporate from my heart. This party was the perfect thing to attend to clear my mind of Ms. Simms. It was being held in Flatbush, in the basement of a church where lots of tables were set up and candles placed in the middle, emitting a warm, romantic glow. The room seemed to be filled to capacity, and I immediately noticed this was definitely an older — or should I just say old — crowd.

I decide to make the best of it and enjoy the ethnic music and culture — Sasha has warned me that I am becoming too Americanized. Suddenly, a man approaches our table.

"Would you like to dance?" he asks.

He is a tall, slender fellow, probably in his late 30s or early 40s. He wears a black suit and an olive-colored dress shirt, which I think doesn't coordinate well with his dark skin. I notice the tribal scarring on his cheeks. It brings immediate images of the rituals that I have read about, which are often performed in different African villages — particularly female genital mutilation, or female circumcision.

The thought puts me in an even greater depressed mood and so I don't feel like dancing, but then my sister interrupts.

"*Ale non.* Go on Marie Claire," she says, nudging me from my seat. Then she turns to the man. "She'd love to dance. I see her moving in her seat." I hate when my sister speaks up for me. "Go dance with the nice man while Marc and I look for Erika," she persists.

I am quickly yanked out of my seat and led onto the dance floor. The room is quite crowded, but this man seems determined to go far into the center, stepping on people's toes and bumping into their groove. We finally station at a cozy corner where three guys are competing for a sister's phone number.

The soca music is hot and spicy and everyone seems to know the words and sings along — everyone except for this man. He immediately draws my waist close to him and attempts to slow dance to this fast tune. We obviously are out of step of the excitement of the others surrounding us, but he is too lost in his own fantasies to notice or care. He starts whispering in my ear.

"How old are you? 21, 22?"

"I'm 13," I reply.

"Oh yeah? You look very mature."

I remain silent as I begin to feel something funny rub against my belly.

"So you're in high school?" he infers.

I am feeling very uneasy at this point, but I respond. "Yes, a freshman."

24

"That's nice, that's nice. Do you like school?"

He proceeds to distract me with more questions, but I begin to feel increasingly nervous and want some air. I push back a little and suddenly he grasps at my waistline even tighter. He won't let me escape his grip and holds me so close to him I felt his erect penis jab my abdomen. The potent smell of his musk cologne nauseates the situation even further.

"What are you doing?" I manage to whisper, despite the large lump that suddenly fills my esophagus. I doubt he hears me. My heartbeat resonates through my ears so loudly I barely hear myself. I become immobilized with panic and disbelief as he continues to rub his pelvis up and down between my legs. I stand motionless and endure what seems like forever. After one last thrust, he finally loosens his grasp. I figure he is "done." Embarrassed (or relieved), he straightens his posture and buttons up his suit jacket to cover up the evidence on his pants.

I walk back to my table feeling abused and violated. How could this man use my body like that? I am only 13, and don't even know yet what it feels like to make out with someone. I remain seated for the rest of the night. I just want to go home.

"Where is my sister?" I think to myself in despair.

She was dancing the night away while I sat there looking lonely and pathetic. I can still feel his imprint on my front, and his scent reeks throughout my clothing. Another guy approaches me.

"Hey baby, want to dance?"

I shake my head. Who are these people, and how could they let such sinful acts occur in the basement of a church? I notice that lots of other women are being groped by other men and some are enjoying it.

Finally, it is time to go home. As soon as I enter the house, I shower and cry myself to sleep. I realize the veracity of what happened and how this incident devastates me. Silently, I shed many tears that night. I cry for the women who tolerate such unconsenting sexual manipulations daily by their disparaging husbands. I cry for the many women who get into far worse conditions, such as rape.

I didn't hate men. My respect for this one was far less, though. In a sad way, he and so many other disturbed males like himself seemed to be taking care of their "needs" and getting away with murder.

I turned my internal anger to action. Initially, it was a mental process that evolved over time and gave birth seven years later... at age 20. But at 13, I fell in love... in love with myself.

From those adolescent years and beyond, I would learn to love the distinctive texture of my hair, the rich mocha and cocoa hues of my complexion, my wide-brimmed nose and full-bodied lips — all genetic trademarks and bonds to my Dahomean lineage. My prolific manner and determinism are characteristic of my African and Haitian ancestors. Eventually I grew closer to the spirit within. I would learn later to grow more complacent with my sexual orientation.

* * * * *

During those questioning years, I had constantly put myself through various situations, thinking maybe I'm just a latent heterosexual. So, have I waited long enough? Now that I'm in my final months of college, I think I'm ready to come out of my shadow. But can I handle IT? IT consists of the prejudice, the phobic hetero people, the possible abandonment from peers who wish to remain ignorant, and the fear of losing all the comforts of "the closet."

That Wednesday, I put all those concerns into perspective and finally attended the Stonewall Coalition meeting at school, which may have changed the rest of my being. I seated myself in the back of room 241, reeling in the ferocious Nancy O'Brien, the school's most out, feminist, pro-choice, protesting lesbian on campus, as she tried to settle down the group members for the meeting. She was quite a popular campus figure, especially when she victoriously petitioned for a new required course called "Gay Men and Lesbians in History: Lives and Legacies" for the school curriculum. She was well-known for her protests on everything from tuition hikes to making the school environmentally aware by getting rid of any Styrofoam cups and plates in the cafeteria, and replacing the note paper being sold in the book store with the recycled kind.

26

Her activism on some other subjects, however, carried through to climactic proportions and has even gotten her arrested. I admired her vigor, but she was a little too butchy for me. In addition to my own personal uncertainties, I had always thought of the organization as more of a political, avenging clique that thrived for attention. I support humanitarian movements for change, but wasn't sure I wanted to get in any kind of trouble for it, as Nancy seemed to be famous for.

"Settle down guys, the Stonewall Coalition meeting will now begin. I'm glad you all were able to attend our first meeting of the year. I'm Nancy, your president, and I want to welcome the new members and old ones to an exciting year."

She passed out the agenda for the fall and continued.

"This calendar keeps you informed of the upcoming events here in the campus and at the Center. For those of you who are unfamiliar with the Center and its resources, I strongly urge you to give them a visit sometime. And for the ladies, try to attend the Lesbian Orientation that will be taking place there tonight, at 7 o'clock. I especially placed that bit of information on the fliers around school today to try to get more women involved in our organization. No offense fellahs, but you can't dominate everything." A light chuckle permeated the room. No offense taken, I'm sure. That was Nancy for you, a true female-conscious hardcore dyke.

"I'd really like to take this opportunity to thank my supporters in last year's elections. I know you all adore me, but I'll be graduating this year, so please respect and pay homage to the suffragists of the past by continuing to vote for the best possible woman... oops, OK, I mean person, who will keep this club alive and running strong for next year, alright?"

As she continued on with the meeting, I wished that I hadn't taken so long in joining this progressive group. She had such an alluring disposition that listening to her speak ignited a spark within me that was irrefutable. I left the meeting and rushed to my next class thinking about the lesbian orientation at the Center that evening. It was something that I knew I had to attend because it was an issue that had been haunting me for so long.

* * * * *

Attending the lesbian orientation at the Lesbian and Gay
Community Services Center was one of those experiences that
can be grouped with the first time you got The Curse, your red
alert, monthly friend, or however you refer to it (just don't say
MENstruation). Or perhaps one can relate the excitement (or
agony) with your first experience wearing a bra. I knew it would
be one of those "firsts" which became a cultivating part of my
womanhood, and this time was no different. I was not ready.

I knew this was an important meeting and that I had to attend,
because something was totally missing in my milieu. Going to
this meeting made me feel closer to my salvation.

Before entering the Center, I was very apprehensive and wary.
I thought about my father and how his perilous stance against the
dictatorship in Haiti cost him his life. He was part of a small clan
who only wanted to declare their feelings and the feelings of
most of the country people as openly and freely in a country that
supressed any oppositional beliefs. In my particular case, I
wanted to do the same; to voice my feelings and opinions to
myself and with a community who felt the same. The difference
was that my country would not persecute me, or would they?

I stood in the autumn chill wondering, "What if someone I
know sees me here, of all places? I'm doomed." But then I
thought, "Well if anyone does see me, what's their defense as to
being at the Center?" It was a double-edged sword.

I bustled my way through the crowd that clumped at the
entrance and walked along the various tables. I listened to the
women of N.O.W., the National Organization for Women, and
the spokesperson from Astraea National Lesbian Action Founda-
tion speak about what kind of group they were and their upcoming events.

"Would you like to be on our mailing list?" one asked.

"With pleasure!" I thought. They were just the type of organizations I needed to join forces with; what I had been searching
for for so long. There are certain perks that accompany the
college experience and one of mine was getting my own mailbox. I took advantage of this since my family constantly gets into

my mail, a cultural tribulation of my Haitian upbringing. Nothing was too personal or confidential according to my mother, not as long as you were a child of hers living under her roof. She loved to open my letters, especially if I was the only one who received any for the day. I would die if I came home and found my mother discovering about my homosexuality through the type of mail that I was receiving.

I hesitantly motioned toward her pen, and then I remembered that this mailbox privilege would only last for the next three months. After that time, the school would begin automatically forwarding your mail to your home address. How soon would it take for my secret to be revealed? I declined and told her I'm just looking around today.

"We understand." I'm sure they did. These women were older, more mature, responsible adults and not the male-bashing, punk, leather-clad lesbians I was used to seeing at school. I wondered how they did it — coming out, that is.

How did these women make their breakthrough? How hard it must have been for them when facilities like the Center weren't around, and everything or anything about homosexuality was something like an underground network with secret code words.

I extended my journey down each table, collecting handfuls of information and pamphlets. Upon listening to a spokesperson speak about a program for lesbian counseling facilities for those with no insurance, the ultimate happened — a Center photographer took a picture of me.

"Oh-my-gosh," I thought, "now my secret isn't a secret for much longer." I couldn't believe it, why me? All I could think of at that point was being on trial with an attorney like F. Lee Bailey demanding, "Were you or were you not, on that fall evening, at a gay community center?" Then he shows the judge, "Let me enter as evidence, exhibit A, this photograph of you with a spokesperson of the blah blah lesbian counseling network." Like Macauley Culkin's famous expression of the Home Alone series: "AAAAHHH!"

It was too late, but was it?

Something inside me turned the entire situation around; I used the incident to symbolize a sort of initiation. The camera flash was my I.D. card into this new world of women lovers, sheroes

29

and truly dignified people who are mocked and scorned because of who they love, and because they are passionate about their beliefs, strong about their values and unified in their mission. And I was now an emerging member.

I resumed my womanist voyage even further. I was feeling more relaxed. I approached a table that had health services for women and pamphlets on safe sex. Lined on the table were Ziploc bags which contained condoms, gloves, dental dams and other goodies. It looked more like getting ready for a root canal than having sex.

"Are these for free?" I asked.

"Yes, take one."

I perused another table where the spokesperson said, "Help yourself to a button." My choice was a black button with a pink triangle in the middle. It would serve as my commemoration pin for gay pride.

Finally, I reached a sincere black woman who told me about her organization called Shades of Lavender. I was delighted to learn that the organization was located right in Brooklyn, close to where my sister resides. She explained that it was an organization entirely run by and for women, with various programs and workshops geared for lesbians and bisexual women of all age groups and ethnicities. "I'm sure that you will find something suitable for your needs. We need to come alive by coming together," she said.

A lecture then followed, with the keynote speaker, Judge Karen Burstein, addressing several issues on women in the gay community. She spoke about her personal bouts in the political forefront since she has come out, but showed little remorse on her recent loss in the election for New York State Attorney General. She was eloquent, assertive, direct, and most importantly, proud, very proud, to be a lesbian. She left me with a feeling of empowerment and instilled a sense of hope to continue on in my search for peace.

A Short Account of My Behavior
by Terri Jewell

My mother once asked me if I had a death wish.

"As if being a female and black aren't trouble enough for you, girl. Now you are talking about dropping out of college? Your father and I have sacrificed a lot to get you into college. I couldn't tell you how long I had to go without a winter coat to put food on the table every day. And you were the Number One student at your high school. Everyone had such dreams for you and now you want to disappoint them. You're going to end up like the others out there with no job or hope for a good life. What on earth has gotten into you? Well, girl, you might as well forget whatever nonsense you think you're going to do. I'M NOT GOING TO ALLOW THAT."

So, I transferred from a university in Kentucky to a small state college in New Jersey to complete the four-year program in what ended up being six years.

Then,

my mother asked me why I bothered to visit home during vacations.

"As if wearing those thick glasses and cutting your hair down to the nub isn't asking for tribulation, girl. Now you're getting fatter and fatter. Don't you care about how you look? Don't you have any pride in yourself? Well, let me tell you something, young lady. You just come back home during your next vacation and I guarantee you will lose some of the weight. And you WILL stay on the diet I put you on. And we will look into getting you some contact lenses. You will look so much better. You have to suffer sometimes to be pretty. You won't regret looking the best you can look. The way you look now, no man will want to be seen with you."

31

I did not go home during vacations. I got a job and my own apartment.

Later,

my mother responded to a letter I had written her.

"As if being fat, black, and a young woman alone isn't dangerous and hell enough. Now you're not shaving under your arms and you say you're a DYKE? My God. Have you gone crazy? Do you hate me that much? I have done nothing but love you, have given you everything you could possibly want, and look how you repay me. Don't you understand where you are? You're not some little white girl who can get away with this. They can play all they want because they don't have the struggle you have in life. They will KILL you just for being alive. You are just begging for death now. You better listen to me, young woman, and find some professional help."

So, I got a white woman psychologist who told me she didn't understand the multiple conflicts I was experiencing with having to speak and act white sometimes. A black woman told me she was primarily a child psychologist who felt that homosexuality was a pathological state. She told me that in all cases such as mine, there was a substance abuse problem in my family. I told her no, that I wanted to see her work through the guilt I felt over my grandmother's death and that I just happened to have a WOMAN as a lover who was as supportive as she could be. Next, I went to a white man psychotherapist who told me to find a boyfriend, get laid and stop worrying about my small problems. I was simply too self-centered and too fat. After that, an East Indian psychiatrist told me that the only thing he could do was to prescribe antidepressants. I advised that that would not be a good idea.

Yet,

my mother thought I had not tried hard enough to solve my

32

dilemma.

"As if being a crazy bulldagger is not bad enough for you. I can't have you as MY daughter. I am so ashamed of you, I can't mention your name to the women at work who are always talking about their daughters. And you just HAD to get a WHITE woman. Going around hugging and kissing the ENEMY. White women get the best of the black men and now they are getting the best of the black women. You are sicker than I care to think about. And you are killing your father, you know that? He doesn't say anything because it hurts him so. You know how hard it is for him to talk about his real feelings. He leaves it up to me to tell you what he feels. I'd rather see you lay down with a dog than lose what's left of your dignity to some white trash heifer. Get out of my sight. And since you know it all, don't bother to ask me for anything since you think you're so GROWN now."

I moved in with my lover, and we grew together.

Still,

my mother called and told me shortly afterwards,

"You just don't care anymore, do you? Are you trying to kill me? How did I fail you? I did the best I could. I had no lessons on how to be a good parent. You may as well blow your brains out. The effect will be the same as what you are doing with your life nowadays. You will never have a decent career. No one will want to hire a Lesbian. Word gets out, you know. You won't have any decent friends. Just perverts who have to live in the very dirt they make for themselves, just like you're doing now. And you won't have any children of your own. Your father's bloodline will end in shame with you. He goes around now, talking about the grandson he'll never have that he wants so much. All that time in school for nothing. JUST LOOK AT YOU. DON'T YOU HAVE ANYTHING AT ALL TO SAY TO ME?"

No, I didn't.

But I did take a good, hard look at myself. And what I found in the mirror was a

big,   strong,

        employed,   capable,   intelligent,

                brown-skinned,   nappy-headed,

                        happy woman in love

                                and in glasses

who was living her life exactly as she pleased.

And Now They Know
by Sheree Slaughter

We thought that this would happen
    Now it's known to be
The truth about this strong devotion
    Shared by you and me

No longer shall we live a lie
    Trying to fool others
For, now it's known we're not just friends
    But, indeed true lovers

The talk shall rise, plenty of stares
    and questions to be asked
We have our answers all prepared
    to complete this revealing task

How could we? Why did we?
    Don't you know it's wrong?
That's what they'll say, but we know else
    and our feelings are too strong

We love the Lord, He heard our cry
    We're reaching forth our hand
Asking, Lord, please have mercy
    please try to understand

We love each other, not more than thee
    For thou art He who sits above
Oh Lord, it's true within our hearts
    Forgive us please, and Bless our Love.

Author's note: This poem was written when I was 14 or 15 years old, during my second relationship. My first relationship cost me nine days in a psychiatric ward; I loved her more than myself.

Be Still and Know
by Brigitte M. Roberts

"Child, what are you doing? Don't you hear that thunder and lightning? Turn off that tv and be quiet."

"But, Momma, I want to watch *Dobie Gillis*."

"I'm going to 'Dobie Gillis' your behind if you don't do like I say. You know better than to be carrying on when it's storming like this. The Bible says, 'Be still and know that I am God.' Girl, you best be still and give God praise, for He is a mighty God, a powerful God, a fearsome God."

"A noisy God," I said under my breath, turning off the tv. Bye-bye Maynard G. Krebs.

She wanted me to see God's magnificence in sound and fury. Wanted me to fear the Lord of Sodom and Gomorrah, the God who turned Lot's wife into a pillar of salt. She wanted me to cower before the Father who so sorely afflicted Job. I believed in another God. The God of lute and tambourine in David's Psalms. I trusted and abided in the God who provided manna to the children of Israel. I was still and reverent in the magnificence of rainbows, waterfalls, mountains, a baby's cry, my aged dog's gentle passing from this place to God's bosom.

"Be still and know that I am God." Whenever it rains I hear Momma's command. Did she think she was God? I turn up the stereo, or wash my dishes, or read *On Our Backs*. Occasionally I reach for my pocket-sized *Gideon's New Testament* (with Psalms and Proverbs) and read of God the Father, the Son, and the Holy Ghost.

> For God so loved the world
> that He gave His only begotten Son
> that whosoever believeth in Him
> should not perish but have
> everlasting life.

37

For God sent not His Son
into the world to condemn the world
but the world through Him
might be saved.

JOHN 3:16,17

Whosoever, Momma, not just the straight, childbearing, churchgoing folks. Whosoever. The pussy loving, clit licking bulldaggers and dick sucking, ass fucking faggots who believe in Jesus will walk beside you and rest at His feet in heaven. I think this and a righteous clap of thunder lets me know Momma is reading my mind and disapproves.

I remember when that thing with Linda blew up. Telephone calls at two, three in the morning. Hangups when Momma answered, whispered arguments when I picked up the receiver. I trusted Momma, but at least once she listened in. One night she reached the phone before I could.

"Girl, you better stop pestering me and my daughter. You best to pray and get yourself right with God. Don't you be trying to teach my child your funny ways, them unholy things. I ain't got but one child and God knows I will do anything to make sure that we will be rejoicing in heaven together, so you best to get over whatever is possessing you. Call here one more time and I will call the law on you, you child molester. Damn you, damn you, damn you ..."

She called Linda everything except a child of God. Momma was so enraged, so blinded by her tears of shame and the knowledge that she had begat a Sodomite that she could not hear me cry, didn't feel me grab at her shoulder, didn't feel me pry the receiver from her hand. She did not respond to my own tears, choked breath, did not recognize me until I had slapped her soundly across the face and still, she shouted at the phone, "Damn you, damn you, damn you," as if that would correct me, make me desire men, make me the hapless victim of the butch on the other end of the line.

"Funny," she said, "I will not have anyone say my one child is funny. I'll have Deacon Carter pray about this. You will fast.

38

Mother Robinson will counsel you. You can't be too far gone. I would've known. And I know it wasn't your fault, baby. We'll take it to Jesus."

I was black, twenty-one, but far from free. I knew the truth but was too frightened to tell her. I wasn't "funny." I was quite serious in my adoration of the clit, vulva, the taste of the female sex in my mouth. Linda hadn't taught me a thing. She was my first serious affair, but sex partner number ten or twelve. But if prayer and fasting would make Momma feel better, so be it.

I allowed Deacon Carter to counsel me. I studied Leviticus 18:21-24, Deuteronomy 23:17,18, 1 Kings 14:24, 2 Kings 23:7, and Romans 1:27. But I refused to allow him to lay hand on my breasts, my ass, slip his tongue in my ear or mouth. When he threatened to reveal "my sin" to the church I promised to cry rape and named four less determined victims of his godless counsel.

Mother Robinson smelled of Cashmere Bouquet and lavender. She was deaf and nearly blind and requested only that I praise Jesus as she rested her arthritic hands upon the crown of my head. She kissed me on the cheek, and as she left said, "Child, all you got to do is trust God to make it right." I did. I do.

Momma, you taught me to see an image of God when I look in the mirror. You taught me to see God in all things, in every-one. How could He be absent in the faces of the women I've held in my arms? You taught me that God will never forsake me, that He is everywhere. How can He not be here, in a bed I share with another of His daughters?

A crack of lightning illuminates the sky and I know Momma hears me. I know she can feel me questioning, stirring, arguing against those things she thinks are fundamentally true.

Well, I'm still black, closer to thirty-one, and finally, finally free. I'm still her only child and, admittedly, "funny that way." Unless I make a turn for the worse, I'm confident of where I'll be come judgment day. Momma doubts, says I'm proud of my sin, declares that I mock the Lord. I say I praise God in every cunt I've known, tasted heaven most times I've made love.

Lightning followed by thunder. Crashing rain. I close the windows. All right, I will turn off the television. I will be quiet, be still, and know that it is God who put the love for women in my heart.

Bed of Thorns
by Gale "Sky" Edeawo

Sitting three weeks, for the same hours, every day at a lesbian bar in West Los Angeles, with no luck. Bills piling, landlord no longer smiling, car running on air. "Where are the bitches with the money to supplement me? At 40 I still got it going on. Damn, a woman with extra cash sure would be nice. A new one, a confused one, a lonely unhappy one, those are the bitches for me.... I'll take them to paradise, for a price."

7:40 Monday evening is when she entered. The new one. Not at all confused, but obviously searching, wondering who would be the first to interest her. To welcome her into the life.

She ordered a beer, studied her glass, and looked into the wall mirror in time to see the well-polished woman approach her. The bar woman sat next to her, close and in control, smiling as if she knew her. She said, "I am here" — just one of her many theatrical approaches. The newcomer found it most amusing that she herself was appearing so obvious, or could this handsome woman really read minds? A two-hour conversation and a few drinks entered her much too quickly, into the life, and into the hustler's bed...

A bed of thorns, in a room with a ceiling that dripped so much honey it managed to counteract the pain. "I think I'm in love, sure I'll help you with your rent. I think I'm in love, let me buy your groceries. I think I'm in love, do you need cigarettes, car running okay? I love the taste of honey dripping from your ceiling, but in time I pray for you to remove the thorns, because I may not be able to endure the pain."

Months passed and the dripping honey turned to acid rain, the bed became unbearable, the room a place of bondage. The newcomer grew tired of giving, giving, never receiving. Waiting, hurting and crying. Feeling less than, so in time she too left. Angry with herself for not knowing of this woman's reputation, she made a mental note to always require references for future encounters.

Back again, sitting alone at the lesbian bar, waits the hustler. Waiting, while thinking to herself, "Well, she was a useful bitch while I had her. Now I must wait for another one. Bills piling, landlord no longer smiling, car once again running on air." Counting the dollars from her final unemployment check, looking unhappily at her fingernails, long in need of their regular manicure. She cautiously took a glance at her profile in the adjacent mirror; she was satisfied with all but her coiffure, which was usually done weekly, but weekly trips to the beauty parlor at this time would be financial suicide.

"Damn, where are all the bitches with the money, or the plastic, that will supplement me. I got it going on, still kicking at 40, I'll take them to paradise, for a price."

At 8:15 Wednesday evening, she entered. Looking a little uncertain, as she made her way to the seat at the bar. "Huh, a confused one, perfect for me, the matronly kind, probably in an unhappy marriage, to a man. Living in a house, with two children, a two-car garage, credit cards and bank accounts.

"I'll wait until she orders her drink, and pays for it, then I'll make my approach."

The matronly woman paid for her white wine and commenced to sip slowly, as she began to question her own uncertainties. "Why am I here? I have a family, a profession and a lovely home... What is missing in my life? Sure my husband plays on me, what married man doesn't? At least he supplies a steady income, and that is more important than steady sex. His being tired all the time is also not an issue; after all, he is working two jobs. I'll finish this wine and get the hell out of here.

"What made me come here anyway? I have been out of this life for over a decade. I have time on my hands, so I'll stop by the library and do some studying, or better still, I'll go to a movie."

Suddenly, she realized that someone had quietly invaded the space next to her. There sat a strikingly attractive woman, very sure of herself, flashing a come-to-me smile, with eyes full of promises. If the matronly woman had only felt or heard the warning signals from the bar patrons and bartenders, who had given audience to this very scene so many times before, she would have jumped up and ran to safety. But it was too late; she

42

was captivated. There were no other surroundings, only this aggressive female sitting comfortably with her back against the counter, looking directly in her face as if they were the only two people in existence. Feeling her weakness, the aggressive woman reached out slowly and lightly touched the back of the matronly hand, leaning closer seductively said, "Are you looking for ME...."

Bird of Paradise
by Alexis De Veaux

Dig One:

Up here on the fourth floor is cold with a hint of spring to come
Camille's first month back in Harlem. Snow falls a thin cantata
against their windows in the light of night light. Under her pink
pastel nightgown the mother Phelia stretches. Her hand fine as
gold dust powder runs along her stomach over her navel. This
umbilical cord of feelings the body never forgets the rip of tissue
that was childbirth. After she said her piece Camille waited for
Phelia to speak.

Where you meet her?

She's from Kingston.

She dig up stuff too?

No. She's a singer. You'll like her.

Don't tell me who to like.

She turns her back to the daughter. In the only bed their match-
box apartment ever had so they shared it all these years. Shared
the habits of sleeping that were a comfort without question to
each of them from the first day Phelia brought Camille home
from the hospital. Phelia's still opened eyes blaze a blackness
with the grip of quicksand. She did not have to like what she
didn't understand. Like how the child spoke French fluently. The
big words Camille used that made her feel stupid. The names of

rocks and stones that fell easily from Camille's young lips. And this. Laying beside her. A woman. With a woman for a lover. Was she going to be happy? Have children of her own one day? Know when it was time to let them go?

When Camille awakes abruptly it is 5am. Her mother is not in bed.
Phelia?
Is not in the bathroom. Or the kitchen down the hall.
Phelia?

Is barely lit with the light of morning the small livingroom holds against a somber blue wall. Phelia is a shadow on the edge of the sofa. She flicks her cigarette in an ashtray atop the coffee table.

You coming back to bed?
All that education you got girl
you aint' learned to sleep by yourself yet?

Camille stands in the livingroom doorway. Everything in this room she thinks everything the television sofa and matching armchair the shelves of knick-knacs and Atlantic City momentos the white lamps and mahogany endtables the pictures of herself and Phelia the one picture of her father everything including the window and this arched doorway has gotten doll house small the two years she's been away digging up evidence of escaped slaves and maroon societies deep in the hills of Jamaica. Some bones don't want to be dug up Camille thinks but does not say. Some animals eat their young.

Dig Two:

It was the first room she stopped in every day after school. She'd sprawl on the bed. Stare at the chiseled face of her great grandmother framed in the faded black and white Civil War photograph staring back at her from the wall. It was Phelia's face in there. In the history of those coal black cheeks. In her needle sharp gaze carved by the meanness of slavery. In this alcove of a room in the afternoon quiet when Phelia had the day shift at the bar the redskinned moon faced girl entertained herself making up stories. About the dark glass bottles of Shalimar Perfume and lavender waters her mother kept atop the maple vanity chest. And the love letters from Camille's father Phelia kept in the bottom drawer. Stories about who he was half Cherokee. How Phelia said he was built like a boxer. Walked low to the ground. Like that night at the bar when Phelia met him. He said he was from N'Awlins and preferred the name Talking Brook to Curtis. And then one day he said baby I got to go.

Dig Three:

How come you don't have no lover Phelia?

Had your father.

What about now?

All I want now is for you to finish college. Become a famous archaelogist like you want to.

That's all you want?

Whatchu want Camille?

To know how you feel.

I feel tired when I get off work.

Dig Four:

When Phelia came home from work she went straight to the bathroom. To wash off the smell of bar stories and tips. In the steam of the shower she'd rinse clean of the night's back and forth on her feet. Juggling glasses and broken conversations. From one side of the bar to the other. Pouring drinks. Mixing one part liquor to three parts I'm a damn good barmaid proud of what

47

I do. Which kept them fed and clothed. With a roof over their heads. Whenever Camille needed extra money for books Phelia laid on the table what the girl's scholarship did not cover. The longed for getting it done done now.

Dig Five:

At the kitchen window the evening quarter moon watches Camille watch Phelia scrape what is left of her dinner into the garbage can. Watches as the daughter turns the mother turns in the orbit of motherhood.

Bring your friend by the bar Phelia says
time for me to meet her.

Who knows when the front door closes behind Phelia gone to work what the moon sees in the afterbirth of mother-daughter love. What stars feel in the quiver of its throat. What a shard of moon sees on the breast of night.

Dig Six:

When Phelia opened the door she saw it right away. On the kitchen table. Was a note from Camille. And the one bird of paradise its royal plumage orange and electric purple in a glass vase next to the note was a flower she had never seen before. Phelia sat down at the table staring at it. Secretly tickled. It was just like Camille. Something new to see whether she understood it or not. She'd done a good job raising the girl alone. There was nothing to regret. In her heart she knew that. And let go.

Bits and Pieces
by Imani Henry

Bile

I am choking on words
that have gone down the wrong way.
Tasting the bile as I chew
on the bits and pieces in my mouth.
An eruption of emotion
produced by cut-off phrases,
sharp, self-righteous sentences
full paragraphs, piercing and pointed.
And I can't remember everything
that was said, ... or maybe I just don't want to.
Anger is so hard to translate.
But I heard you, nevertheless, when you said,
"What about the women?"

I wanted to tell my mother, I am a lesbian.

but there's this voice in my head sayin:

"ARE YOU CRAZY?"

Do you really think you can tell her? Say it out loud, to her face?

How do I do that?

How do the white girls do it?

The I-HAVE-ALWAYS-BEEN-A-DYKE-ones, since I've been in diapers ones.

Uncle so and so is gay ones, mentioned around the dinner table ones.

The house in the Hamptons ones, keeping it out the newspaper ones,

The college experiment ones, it will ruin your career ones,

49

The 2nd generation ones, having two moms ones,

How do I, say to my Jamaican,

Sunday School teaching,

can make a dollar stretch for a whole week,

Pro Life/ Pro War,

"Una tink me a play? I ain't no joke"

MAMA?

So what's a child suppose to do? Clearly something is wrong with the world. I hate my mother,
all females. Everybody does. Everybody says so.
"too weak," "too dumb," "can't drive," "you run
like a girl," "you throw like a girl," that's
what the boys say. Why do i have to be a girl? I
hate frilly, flower, lacy stuff anyway. Ribbons,
bows, white pompoms attached to my sweaters.
Wearing Easter baskets on my head with those
shiny black strapped up shoes. Silent in church,
not even God likes women. It's Eve's fault the
whole is in sin, that's what the Bible says. The
man is the head of the house and nobody tells
him what to do. I hate anybody telling me what
to do.

I want to be a man when I grow up.

One day somebody said, "GIRLS AGAINST THE BOYS!"
and everybody knew where to go, what side they
were on. And I stood there, in the middle of the
playground. I thought,

"Where do I go? I just can't stand here."

I went to the Girls' side because it was the
right thing to do.

The Girls, not used to playing with me, made me
a "spy" and sent me to the Boys' side. And we
stood arms around each other, huddled together.
Making plans and strategy until all of a sudden,

someone looked up and yelled, "Hey, Faith's here!"

"Oh shoot, she's been here the whole time."

Everybody laughed.

"She's been here the whole time and nobody noticed."

More laughter until some of us were laying on the ground.

I don't remember which side won.

Burn:
"IF YOU CAN'T HEAR, YOU'LL FEEL."

There is a burn down one side of my mother's back. She got it when she was a child.

Light to dark brown, the burn is prominent, a covering.

I know she told me the story of how it happened many times, like a parable.

She got it for not listening, not being careful, not obeying. I think it scared me so much that I can't remember the details of how and why. What I have retained is the image of my mother half-dressed, barefoot running down a narrow, rocky lane. Crying, screaming, smelling the smoke,

feeling the flame on her skin.

"IF YOU CAN'T HEAR, YOU'LL FEEL."

My mother is yellow. Pale, semi-pinkish yellow, not that high golden yellow; I wonder all the names they use to describe my mother's complexion? What got said in the school yard? ... Out loud, to her face. Shade, a leading import of colonization.

Born in Jamaica still under British rule. The first of five children. My grandmother, blind since she was twenty-eight. Medical negligence, a nurse put the wrong drops in her eyes; never saw

51

any of her children. My grandfather, a bus driver, cab driver, the man once called "Busha," was now Papa. The first of five, the little yellow girl was the eyes her mother no longer had. The eyes that could see just how poor they were. The little yellow girl saw everything and learned to keep secrets. The oily paperbags with homemade lunches, eaten in far corners of the school yard. The one pair of school shoes dyed tangerine by mistake, making her lead her younger siblings through the back streets home.

The first of five, the little yellow girl, shy, quiet, dignified. The crown of protection she wore. The silence of secrets she bore and she learned to take care of everyone, everything, organize, strategize, make it all happen.

"IF YOU CAN'T HEAR, YOU'LL FEEL."

"I promised myself, I would never do to you children what was done to me," she told me, her firstborn, after the hairbrush she was hitting me with snapped in two across my back. Rage makes ordinary objects dangerous weapons. Handheld, flying towards you. Mixing spoons, brooms, ketch-up bottles ... her bare hands.

"Una tink me and you are size? You a smell up your armpit. I'll tump you down! I'll show you who is the woman in this house!"

There was a woman who was getting dressed on her wedding day. Her mother was hovering, fussing over the smallest detail of preparation. The woman, anxious, trying to gain control, turned to her mother and said, "Mama, Stop It, na!" And with that her mother began to beat her with a belt, because she has never tolerated disrespect and "I'm not gonna start now!"

The woman walked down the aisle, tear-smeared make-up, long red welts showing through the lace. Of course, this is a funny story, because everybody knows Jamaicans are quick-tempered. Everybody knows Jamaicans are violent. Everybody knows Jamaicans are crazy and you just don't mess with them crazy Jamaicans.

The funny part is that nobody ever says, "Mama, Stop It, na!" and the little yellow girl with the burn down her back became the woman who broke promises to herself. Continued to take care of

52

everyone. Never a thought to herself. Still collecting secrets. Displacing her rage, righteous woman's rage, on the back of her firstborn.

She stopped the car and turned to face us in the back seat.

I saw it. That look, the rage. But I am twenty-two and it is him, my little brother, who is the target. He is a child who has struck the last nerve, tested her fragile patience.

"TELL HIM! TELL HIM, I AM NOT PLAYING! Tell him, what you girls used to go through. Tell him, how much it takes for me not to reach over and whack him. I'm trying not to do that anymore."

My sister sits in the passenger seat in silence. I punch my brother's arm. A quick, hard jab. A reflex, learned behavior. A wave of remorse hits me as soon as I make contact.

"Listen to her! She is right. You don't know how lucky you are...," I hear myself say. "We used to get hit all the time. And..." He is not listening. His face is boiling; angry, embarrassed. The corners of his eyes crush hot tears. He rubs the sore spot on his arm and grumbles towards the window. No one can hear anything when they are forced to feel.

The car is back in motion. I stare out the window. I want to cry.

I wondered if she even realizes what just happened?

My mother, with all her children present, had acknowledged the abuse.

The secret out, the silence broken. The promise to herself intact.

But I am in awe of this woman who had learned

that she could not take care of anyone

until she took care of herself.

Burns with time do fade.

I am recovering.
Changing my shirt, trying to settle my stomach.
Thinking about, "well, if only, ... I could of, ...
She should of, ... well maybe not."
cuz everything is evrythang,
and has a rhyme and reason.
All the screaming, the hurled one-liners
the sighs of frustration.
But I heard you, nevertheless, through our
stalemate of silence, when you said,
"Have you ever loved a woman before?"

I wanted to tell my mother, I am a lesbian.
But there's this voice in my head sayin:
"ARE YOU READY TO BE DISOWNED?"
Do you really think you can tell her? Say it out loud, to her face?
Could she handle it? Could I handle it?

A seven-foot Christmas tree, heavy on the garland and flashing
lights. Presents stacked past the branches. The Mormon Taber-
nacle Choir's "Joy to the World" blares in the background as we
all gather in the living room. My wife and I, dreadlocks flowing
down our backs, are dressed in matching red turtlenecks. My arm
around her shoulder, her head resting against mine. My father,
camera ready, calls out, "Choops, Choops," motioning for us to
kiss. My partner, camera shy, kisses me and then giggles into my
neck. The focus is now the chubby baby girl, with kinky un-
tamed hair, stomping across the room. My father catches a shot
of the toddler as she collapses into her grandmother's lap. My
mother scoops up her "Bunga Baby," squeezing her tightly.
Silently thankful for her first grandchild, my daughter. My sister
stops a moment from her job of passing out the presents to smile

at a friend. The first woman she has brought home that has been more than a college roommate. My brother, always the comedian, is cracking jokes. As usual, he and my partner, full of sarcasm, banter back and forth. Their friendship special, developed over time. He being the first to welcome her into the family. At my father's suggestion, we gather for a group picture. As he pans each face with the camera, there is love and happiness in our eyes. The music grows louder as we settle into position. And with the final stanza, in unison, we exclaim, "CHEESE!"

The scene fades to black.

Credits Roll.

But who am I fooling?

I am sitting in an empty diner. From behind the counter, the cook is complaining about having to work on Christmas Day. In front of me, there is a plate of half-cooked turkey, a side of mashed potatoes and a creamed vegetable. I believe it is corn. As I down my fourth beer, I hear William Schafner croon "The Little Drummer Boy." The cook quickly flips the radio to the all-talk station. There is a man ranting about "welfare mothers stealing his Christmas bonus." I order another beer.

I haven't seen my family in over a year. I've tried calling, to at least hear a voice, then hang up. But their number is now changed and unlisted. I have heard my father is following through with the counseling. It was that or jail time, which wouldn't have been much anyway. The judge was pretty lenient considering the charge was attempted murder. From his bench, the judge kept shaking his head and sighing as the proceedings went on. In his closing remarks, he commented, "What a shame to see a family torn apart like this. I have a son, you know, about her age. I just don't know what I would have done, either, if he told me he was a faggot."

My mother, the good Christian woman that she is, corrects my father when he insists he only has two children. Only when she is asked about me, replies with, "Oh, she's very, very sick. We don't like to talk about it. Just please, pray for her." My sister I have seen: on TV. Now an outspoken activist, appearing on all the daytime talk shows. Her campaign message: "How Racism, Sexism and Homosexuality is what's wrong with America today!" My brother, last I heard, is considering taking his young men's ministry to San Francisco.

Most of my scars have healed. They say it may take a while before I regain the use of my left arm. But none of that matters, because for the first time in my life, I would give anything to wake up at 9:00am on a Saturday morning for family Bible hour.

So what's a child suppose to do? When the world brings training bras and the fear of God once a month. Now I can't pick sides — I am a girl ... and that's that. Please be my friend, girl ... so we can sit on the bench and watch the boys shoot hoops for us. Sit in the corner and giggle, to see if he's watching. Talk among ourselves, talk behind her back. "Girl, she think she's cute." "She's been killin that same dress all year." "Girl, she need to do somethin with that hair, rake it or somethin." I hear them whisper as I close the bathroom door.

Now I'm pretty enough, so I'm told, trying to finish my end of the conversation as he looks through me, up my skirt, talking to my breasts. He don't hit me, so that's respect. So is this what it's like being a girl?

I get so nervous in the locker room changing my clothes. Is everybody staring at me? Did she see me staring at her? You got to be careful not to get caught looking. Everybody is racing in and out of their clothes like we're supposed to be ashamed or something. Once dressed, tight shirts, short skirts, made-up, hair just right, now it's OK ... for the boys ... it's all right for the boys to stare.

One summer at Christian camp, it was my favorite year. Denise, Pam, Liz, Kathy ... eight of us girls, did everything together. Shared our clothes, secrets. Running free in the woods, walking around naked in the cabin. The last night of camp, three to a bunk, cuddled together so no one falls out. Back home, writing letters once a week, then once a month, then it was like we never met. Denise, the last letter, you wrote me, the one where you lost your virginity to the guy on the football team. I never told you ... I was hurt.

One day, I was sitting on the bus, coming back from one of them pilgrim places, and I look over at this girl sitting across from me. Her neck was so long, slender, really pretty. I want to reach over and kiss her, right on her neck. Oh my God, what am I thinking? I can't do that ... right? I mean, I'm not suppose to. Would she let me? Could I kiss her if I was a boy?

Eyes, big brown, watching me like a tiger stalks prey.

"You can't lie girl, with those eyes." Your eyebrow raised. Giving yourself away, telling on you. Your eyes speak the words you can't say. I am drowning in your eyes, your smell. Rose petal, oatmeal soap against your skin, smooth and hard. Thick body, hips stacked on tight thighs, calves built up. My nose is pressed to your belly, my tongue follows, tasting soap and sweat. Circling wide nipples, nibbling your neck, fingers tracing the arch of your spine.

I thought I'd suffocate. Your tongue deep inside my mouth, deep inside me. Needing to catch my breath, wanting to lose consciousness.

I lay next to you for the first time. Your head pins my shoulder blade. Shiny, black short hair bristling my chin. I don't want the sun to come up, shine through my window. I kiss your forehead to hear you moan again, crack a smile, nuzzle my breast.

You awake, abrupt, panting. "What is it, baby?" Another nightmare.

I wrap my body around you, trying to pull you to me. Your back rigid, muscles defined. I sit up with you, my thighs surround your buttocks. Rocking you gently, stroking your hair, as you remember. I want to make it stop, make sweet love to you until the memories fade. Until it's safe to dream again.

You are so restless. Hands quick, as your temper. Your swagger defiant. Rough neck, rude girl, La Borinqueña. The fire in those eyes, red hot, flames ignited, "What the fuck you looking at?" He bumps into you, staring at me, sizing you up. "Let it go, honey," I whisper, as those eyes burn with rage, hands curved into fists.

"Are you a man or a woman?"

"A man," you tell your boss, eye to eye, dead on, your stare of survival. Cracking a smile, trying to forget the last nightmare, remembering there is someone waiting at home.

"I'm afraid," as honest as you'll ever be. I don't have to look into your eyes. But you turn away, so I can't see. I know too much anyway. Cautious, cat-like eyes, every time I say "I love you." Soft, water-filled eyes, like the time your mother chased you with a knife. Dry, tearless eyes, as your stepfather lay on top of you at night.

"I'M AFRAID," you scream now after each nightmare, pulling my arms away, pinning down my shoulder blades, pushing me into the wall. Your eyes, burning, red-hot, tiger-like, steadfast, dead on, "GET OUT OF MY HOUSE! TAKE YOUR SHIT AND LEAVE!" My hands quick, wrapped around your throat, curved into fists.

Yeah, my mother didn't raise no fool. I come from the same place you do.

Yeah, we both know rage. Blocking the blows, the sting of the switch, throwing punches before you are hit.

Violence begets violence, but "Baby, I don't want to live

like this. I don't want to go back there. Please come with me."

And for the first time, your eyes say nothing.

Headache

Lord, only You one know.

My daughter is a rebel. Everything we believe in, she is against. Always going off about this thing and that, some political cause or another. She has dreadlocks now and she wonder why she can't find a job. And she know how her father and I feel about them. She lives in New York, she works with people with AIDS, she's been to Cuba ... I said a long time ago, "I don't understand her, I just accept her." And leave the rest up to God.

We have gotten closer over the years. After all the fighting, her disobedience, disrespect. She was so terrible to us, to me. Now, my daughter calls me her friend. I don't know what that means, she's still my daughter, but it true that we are closer. We talk more now. She tells me more. I know more about her. There are things I know about her, that I have heard from other people. Like when she had a boy in the house when we went on vacation. There are things that I know because mothers just know their children.

She called me one night. It was a very hard time for her, you know. She had gotten evicted from her apartment and we tried, called friends in New York, trying to find a place for her to stay. It's not easy on them in New York. It's not easy for us, here in Boston. She finally got a place, really cheap rent but it needed lots of work, she said. Anyway, she called to tell me that she had to move again. She said that she and the woman she had been living in the apartment with got into a fight. The woman had stolen her rent money from her and now the landlord was kicking her out. She was crying, bawling. Not about being kicked again, from another apartment. But how this woman had hurt her. Carrying on with "Why?" and "How could she do this

59

to me?"

"Why did you let her stay with you in the first place?" I asked her. She said the girl had no place to live. "So what, how can you help somebody when you don't have nothing for yourself?"

She started preaching politics. Homeless people, Homeless people with AIDS, Housing should be a right, Budget cuts, Medicaid cuts, Welfare cuts, something about "Russia under Capitalism," I don't remember what she said or what I said. I was yelling, she was yelling and it went on for over an hour.

What I did know was that cry. I have heard my daughter cry like this before. The same "Why?" and "How could ... how could *he* do this to me?" Don't ask me when I started to suspect it. I just had a feeling over the years. I had hoped that I was wrong and maybe it wasn't true. Even then, over phone, with us screaming at each other, I didn't want to think about ....

"SAY IT, SAY IT, MOM, JUST SAY IT!" she screamed at me over the phone.

"I DON'T KNOW, WHAT DO YOU WANT ME TO SAY?"

"YOUR BIBLE TEACHES YOU THAT PEOPLE LIKE ME SHOULD DIE!"

"I don't know what you are talking about," I told her.

Finally, she lets me off the phone. I was exhausted, but I wanted to call her back and yell "**I AM YOUR MOTHER. OF COURSE I KNOW. BUT THAT DOESN'T MEAN I WANT TO KNOW.**"

I left it alone, neither us brought it up again. Months later I get a call from her.

"Mom, I really want to tell you something. Maybe I should write a letter. Maybe you already know what it is. Well, anyway, I'm coming to town, next month. Can we maybe go somewhere and talk?"

and my head started pounding as soon as I put down the receiver.

Next day, I didn't feel all that well
but got out of bed anyway
Head pounding, replaying the words
over and over again,
reacting to, retracting, still retaining
bits and pieces, tasting the bitterness
in the mouth, now silent in disgust,
wanting no noise, no voices, especially
not hers, or mine,
for there is nothing left to say.
For I keep hearing you, nevertheless when you said,
    "Can you love me?"

I get in the car. We do the quick-in-the-front-seat hug. There is always tension when she picks me up from the train station. I smell of cigarettes. My hair has grown longer, more natty. I am not a Christian and thus damned to hell — the usual. So, this is it. I going to tell my mother that I am a lesbian. No more excuses. Trying to pinpoint her reaction. I want to do this. This the right thing to do. I am ready. I feel strong enough. I can accept the consequences. I can outrun her if I have to.

I can do all things through Christ that strengthens me.

Lord, please get me through this. I just buried my father. The whole family went. She was only one who didn't come to Jamaica for the funeral. I am tired, you know. I just worked all day long and I'm too tired to "go somewhere and talk." Lord, please don't let it be what I think it is.

61

She is sitting down at the other end of the bench. She is clutching her purse, like I'm going to rob her. What? She has never asked about my politics before. Exactly what are they? I don't get it, why are we talking about welfare mothers stealing her tax dollars? Oh, she is really angry at me for not going to Grandfather's funeral. No, she is just really angry. This is not a good time to talk. This was a mistake. I want to go home.

Why am I out here, in the first place? I have a million things to do at home. She thinks the whole world revolves around her. I have two other kids at home, you know. Both of them put together don't give as much trouble as this one does. Hurry up! Tell me! My head has been pounding for the last two days. Ever since you called to say you were in town. I can barely keep from crying. Get it over with! I am tired. I tired of being hurt by you. I just want to go home.

Mama, please don't stop loving me.

I don't want to lose you after everything we've been through.

All the fighting, the boxing matches.

I just wanted us to be closer.

I don't want to have to lie anymore, hide things from you.

Mom, you don't know how hard it's been.

I should of sent you the letter, the first one, I wrote in my journal.

But NO!!, that wasn't good enough,

so I wrote a six-page essay that I shared with the woman I was dating,

which led to a big argument because

we were too different to be dating in the first place,

that inspired a poem about

"choking on words that have gone down the wrong way,"

which somehow made me believe

I was actually strong enough to sit here
on this stupid park bench, with my mother,
while you keep telling me to lower my voice
so the stupid golfers playing 20 feet away
won't hear me talk about ...
desperate secret crushes to full-blown denial.
I am wicked and sinful, crazy and diseased.
Isn't that right, Mama?
"THE WAGES OF SIN IS DEATH."
That's what the Bible says.
That's why God blew up Sodom and Gomorrah.
Sending down fire and brimstone
upon the city of sin.

"THE WAGES OF SIN IS DEATH."
That's what the Bible says.
But If they were so bad, Mama. If it was so
wicked?
then why did she look back?

There they were. Husband and wife.
Running, dodging the falling debris,
flames showering from the skies.
Fleeing for their lives.
What was she thinking?
What had gone through her mind?
when he proclaimed it was God's will to
leave her home behind.

There they were. Husband and wife.

Running, hearts pounding with each stride.
Hearing the buildings crackle,
the blood-curdling cries.
What was she thinking, Mama?
Your Bible never said.
Had she found fulfillment, love
in that city of the dead?
What was that something or someone?
What she had wanted, needed
beyond mere lust or desire?
Was it imprinted in her nature
that she turn around to face the fire?

"THE WAGES OF SIN IS DEATH."
Yes, I heard you Mama!
Now will you please tell me
What that poor wicked woman
looked back there to see?

Had this nameless sinful woman
defined by her lot
defied god and man
to see if her woman
had made it out?

She pulled up to the train station.

"What did you expect me to say?"

She had asked this question earlier. Too engrossed in the process, I had forgotten to answer.

This time, I heard the gentleness in her voice. I looked at my mother. Her expression, pleading, as if you needed to know, "Did

I do alright?"

Of course she knew. Even though it was hard for her to hear, have it confirmed. But she was more angry, hurt that it was kept a secret for so long.

"You mean to tell me the whole world knows except for your family?"

"Don't expect me to accept it!" she had said, but there was no lecture of hell and damnation, no rage displaced, no tears and sackcloth.

"What did you expect me to say?"

"I don't know. You're the only parent I've ever come out to."

"When are you going to tell your father? Don't expect me to do it!"

"NO, don't tell him, I mean, I never thought I would be able to tell you. I could see me years from now, married with children still ..."

"You mean to tell me...," she interrupted.

"... to a woman, we can do that, you know," I lied.

She said nothing. I knew she must be struggling with this new image of my wedding day.

But her face, that beautiful, yellow face, remained calm and affirming.

"I love you, Mama"

"I love you, too"

Another in-the-front-seat hug. Not as quick.

I got out the car and headed towards the token booth.

My mother later told me that she started crying as soon as I left the car.

Halfway home, she had to pull over.

I feel better today.
No more churning in my stomach
Can taste the flavors of food,
the sugar and salt distinguished in my mouth
Still holding on to a noun or two,
I haven't forgotten
Needing to conjugate a verb,
but like I said before
Anger is not my best language.
No more, "What if," "Should of," "could of"
cuz we're beyond that.
Wanting to hear your voice and mine
say, "I'm sorry"
begin to mend the broken bond
heal fractured feelings
because I heard you,
nevertheless, even what you couldn't say
I just hope you heard my answers.

Black Triangles, Rainbows and Dykes
by L.K. Barnett

The triangle was my absolute favorite shape in kindergarten.
When our teacher usta hold up big white signs with colorful
shapes on them I would save my breath, my voice, until she held
up the white sign with the black triangle on it. When she asked
"... and what sign is this?" I would nearly scream "TRIANGLE!"

I don't know why I developed a fascination for triangles. I
guess circles were just too round and squares were just too
confining. My love for triangles followed me through elementary
school. In junior high I won first place in an art contest because I
made a collage out of various ethnically diverse faces I'd cut out
of magazines. My collage was shaped like a triangle with a
rainbow border surrounding its isosceles edges.

In high school, my family and I found out I was dyslexic, so
they put me in this stupid remedial reading and language arts
program. I was, however, allowed to continue in the honors
Geometry. It was really cool being in a class full of juniors and
seniors who stumbled into class whenever they wanted, reeking
of reefer and sometimes even alcohol.

My senior year of high school I went to my mother's
girlfriend's art gallery opening. Suzanne, my mom's friend, gave
this speech on the importance of promoting contemporary art;
afterwards people started roaming around the gallery, talking to
each other in that stupid *I'm-a'wanna'-be-intellectual* way. A
huge picture of a solid black triangle on a rainbow surface
caught my attention. I walked over to the picture and just stared.
I was so overwhelmed by the picture and my desire to compre-
hend its meaning, I didn't notice that I was standing very close to
a drop-dead beautiful woman — until she sneezed.

"Bless you," I said. Curious, I asked her, "What do you think
this means?"
"It doesn't really mean anything," she said. "It's more like a
token of appreciation."

Her tone of voice was so matter-of-fact I decided she must be
the artist.

"I love it," I said as I extended my hand. "My name is Dorie."

"Thanks. And my name is Barbara," she said, firmly gripping my hand.

"You said this painting is a token of appreciation?"

"Yes, to Jewish women who were brave enough and proud enough to be truthful about their sexual preferences. In Nazi concentration camps, Jewish lesbians were forced to wear upside-down black triangles, and we have kept the symbol alive within the lesbian and gay community. The rainbow is a modern-day symbol of gay pride. Before I started this painting, I read a book about the persecution of gays and lesbians during the Nazi era. I grieved for weeks after reading the book; then I decided to channel my grief into something positive. I began to feel proud of the women who endured all that pain and strife — just because they were lesbians and Jewish."

It was getting late and my parents were ready to leave the art gallery. I didn't want to leave because I was enjoying talking to Barbara. She was very intelligent and not at all what I thought a lesbian woman would be like. My parents had spoken disapprovingly of gays and lesbians whenever footage from some gay march or something was on television. And my mom always escorted me to the beauty salon and to the shopping mall because she didn't want her daughter getting her hair cut "too short" or buying too many pairs of 501s. After all, she said, I didn't want to look like "one of those women."

Well, Barbara didn't look like "one of those women" at all. Her dark ringlet-hair fell in cascades over her small shoulders, leaving barely an inch-or-so of delicate neck to be seen. Her frame was petite but curvaceous. She wore a pair of corduroys which hugged her hips and firm butt and a turtleneck that clung to her bra-less small chest, advertising nipples that were unmistakably proud of their existence. Everything about Barbara was feminine.

I told Barbara good-bye, and she gave me one of her cards and said if I ever wanted to have coffee and talk, to give her a call.

Later on that night, after I'd had my shower and recalled Barbara's face a million times, I began to think about the personal bond I'd always had with triangles and if in any way it was related to my subconscious desire to bond with women. I was, after all, the only senior girl who had never been out on a date with a guy — according to my mother. I just wasn't into boys. But I'd never considered the *other*. I said my prayers and turned out the light. I thought about Barbara some more before I got out of bed to retrieve her card from the back pocket of my Levis. I folded the card until it formed a tiny triangle and I went to sleep with it safely enclosed in my fist.

cabaret
by mistinguette

Neicy's in the bathroom
with a knife! Even over
the dance floor thunder
you could hear her wailin
like a baby wants her ma:
I'ma kill yall if you come in here Got
dammit whatchu lookin at? I'ma
kill yo black ass, ya hear me? Women
lined up three deep on tiptoe
hopin for a peek inside at
this weeks object of Neicy's violent desire.
Her long white dress hiked up cheap synthetic lace
in the unkind light of 100 unshaded watts &
I did feel ashamed for staring
as mascara, tears and snot ran all down
her reflection in the mirror,
but I didn't turn away.
Big Helen came through
300 pounds of dangerous femme, armed with only
a beaded bag and too much Bal A Versailles
Give the girl some room she shouted and opened
a path to the door. Which she closed behind her,
knife or no knife, Neicy still screamin in the mirror bout
killing somebody

And the record changed and Al Green said
he was Tired of Being Alone
and a strong hand in the small of my
shoulder made Neicy's howl sound just like
won't you help me girl just as soon as you caa-a-a-a-an
and I didn't wonder about her the whole
long bus ride home. *No more bulldagger balls for me*
I promised as I eased back in the house
Some silly nigger is always in the bathroom
cussin and fightin with somebody else

71

But after I brushed my teeth
I stared at my brown
almost-woman reflection
in the mirror for a real long time
before I turned out the light.

Class Reunion
by Liza Wesley

"Jody, you better get going, it's almost four."

"Okay Mom, I'm going." I gave myself a last look in the mirror. Dark brown face, a few new crinkles at the corners of my eyes when I smiled, and now grey mixed in with the black. It was October and I was home in Philadelphia for my high school class' 20th reunion. Mom stepped into my old bedroom to inspect my choice of garb for the evening.

"Well, at least you don't dress like a stevedore for school anymore."

"Thanks a lot, Mom." At age 16, I was given to wearing plaid flannel shirts and blue jeans, hence the stevedore remark. Thank God Mom didn't see the tux I wore to the 10-year reunion! Now I wore my favorite dress pleated gray pants, a burnt orange shirt and a blazer.

"Okay Mom, I might be back very late. Some of us girls might want to hit a club later."

"Well be careful, Baby."

I was a musical student athlete at Mt. Airy Prep for Girls. Most of my friends were fellow orchestra and band members, or choir members; the rest were athletes. I knew everybody though: the heads, the nerds, the born-agains, and the girls who brought their girlfriends to the prom. I had missed the prom.

Truth be told, few friendships had survived the years. Cheryl Bass was my best friend even though she lived in Michigan. Through her I kept track of several alums. Sort of like "telephone." The two of us had sworn to make the big 20th-year reunion. Of course, there were other women with whom I exchanged Christmas cards or the seasonal chatty note.

I parked in the Adam's Mark lot and walked into the hotel. Anita Baines was manning the reception table outside the hall.

"Dr. Jody Gross, good to see you, Lady!" We gave each other a warm hug.

"Anita, how are you girl?"

"Oh I'm fine. How's your mom?"

"She's fine, your dad?"

73

"He keeps talking about moving to Florida."

"Who's in Florida?"

"Nobody. See the problem?"

"Hmm ..."

At the reception table, there was a spread of buttons. The buttons were actually our senior yearbook photographs.

"Here's you, Jody."

"I haven't worn my hair like that since college." The button featured my smiling visage wreathed by an enormous afro. Now my hair was closely cropped but still natural.

"You aren't the only one. Get inside and see our class."

"I'll catch you later, Anita."

I walked through the doors into the great hall. Everywhere there were women. The Class of '76 had 276 girls in it, and most of us were expected. As my class was by and large straight, there were quite a few males — er, men. I looked for old friends, familiar faces.

Girls transform into women. It's funny but the change is most profound in straight women. They marry and their faces reveal possession. They breed and their bodies record the event. With a deep breath I waded across the room towards my classmates. Abby Bennet was the first recognizable face.

"Jody Cross, Ph.D.!" Abby's foxlike face turned up to me.

"Abby Bennet, M.B.A., how's the money, honey?" We laughed. "Are you still at Lincoln Bank?"

"No girl, I left them almost seven years ago. I've been at Blue Cross ever since."

"So what do you do?"

"I'm regional chief in charge of operations in the Delaware Valley."

"Go on, girl!"

"Go on yourself, Jody. I heard you interviewed on NPR. That muscle fiber stuff. I turned to a friend and said, 'Mt. Airy Prep Girl all the way.'"

"You know it. Hey, where's Cheryl?"

Abby looked about. "Haven't seen her, but you find her and tell her black butt to say hello."

"You got it." I moved off to find other faces. As I passed women, our eyes would go to our buttons and then our faces.

74

Funny how much we had changed. Thank God for those picture buttons! I found Cheryl; she was with Rose Lewis.

"Cross, it's about time!" Cheryl hugged me hard.

"Give me a break, Miss Bass; I made it. Hey Rose, what's up?"

"Same ole same ole. Good to see you, Jody." We hugged affectionately.

"You guys gotta say hello to Abby."

"Oh, what she say? 'Tell Cheryl to get her black butt over here?' " Cheryl asked.

"How well we know each other," I replied. We three chatted for a while. Cheryl was a music educator in Ann Arbor, Rose a corporate lawyer in San Francisco.

"You know Rose, I envy you living in San Fran."

"Jody, it is lovely, but I actually live in Oakland. San Fran houses are too high."

"I heard that!" Cheryl emphatically agreed.

I moved on after more chat. There was a good-sized crowd clustered around a strikingly tall beauty. Our class had two celebrities: Gabriella Sorens, a mezzo-soprano, and Dr. Barbara Sanders. Barbara, a psychologist, was known nationally for her treatise "Overcoming the Culture of Abuse." We had been friends, and every year exchanged Christmas cards and chatty notes. At 6-foot, Barbara had 4 inches on me. She was golden brown in hue. In '76 her hair was shoulder-length and bouncing. Now it was in a relaxed, curly style. Tonight, she wore a lavender pleated full-length skirt and a soft gray blouse; over her shoulder was flung a woolen jacket. Barbara still had that sleek swimmer's build — that powerful lifeguard's physique. I had to smile when I remembered how we used to play "lifeguard."

"Jody, let me practice lifesaving on you," she would advance on me.

"There's no pool in the gym, Barbara," I would hold my ground.

"I know that. I have to practice breaking victims' holds."

"Victims?"

"Here's what you do: Grab me as hard as you can, you're drowning you know. Hold me tight, and I'll do the rest."

I stared at her and she smiled, not completely reassuringly. I

75

don't know why, but I would always comply. I would put her in a bear hug, pinning her arms to her side. Barbara would grunt and then slither her arms out of mine. Those lifeguards must learn these secret wrestling moves, because invariably I would end up down on the mat with my head in a quarter nelson. Once the P.E. instructor found us thus. I can only guess what she must have been thinking.

"Thanks Jody, that was great," Barbara would breathe into my ear.

I shook off that memory and went to find others I might recall as friends. There was a girl I had played clarinet with in junior high and high school!

"Rita! Good to see you!" I resisted the urge to hug her, as ours had been a less physical friendship.

"Jody!" Her quiet accountant's face lit up and her arms opened wide.

I gladly hugged her back. "Girl, you look good." I smiled at my pleasantly plump band co-member.

"Thanks, Jody. Why are you still slim after all these years?"

"Oh stop, Rita. Tell me how it goes with you."

"There isn't much to say. I've been married to George 10 years now, two kids."

"Stop right there Rita, nowadays that's a lot."

She gave me a little smile. "Thanks, Jody. I've gone out on my own; left the accounting firm and have my own business now."

"Rita, it makes me glad to know you're an independent CPA like my dad."

"Oh, I don't know if I'm like your dad. People still mention him down at the IRS. Apparently he had quite the way with them."

"Say no more." We both laughed. Jasmeen, another fellow band member, came over and we three chatted amiably for a while.

Suddenly an arm fell across my neck. I caught a delicious scent of cologne. I knew who it was before her low voice purred in my ear.

"Jody, why must I always come to you?"

I wish I had had a clever reply, but I didn't.

"So good to see our student body prez," Jasmeen said as she

stepped around me to greet Barbara, as if me in a choke-hold deserved no mention.

Barbara didn't miss a beat, or release her hold. "Jasmeen Walker, good to see you. And you too, Rita." She reached out to clasp both their arms.

"Barbara ..." I found my tongue.

"Jody, do you mind?" Barbara scolded me.

Rita and Jasmeen laughed and joined Barbara in very small talk indeed. I gingerly pried at Barbara's forearm, which was distressingly rock hard.

"Barbara, I loved seeing you on the Today Show and telling my coworkers, 'See that Mt. Airy Prep Girl,' " Rita said.

"Thank you, Rita, and when I do my taxes I say, 'Damn, I need a Mt. Airy Prep Girl!' "

We all laughed at that. Rita said to Barbara and me, "I'm going to leave you ladies; I think you have things to discuss."

Jasmeen chimed in, "Couldn't agree more Rita, we're outta here."

Suddenly I was all alone with Barbara Sanders. I looked up at her. She favored me with her trademark incandescent smile.

"Barbara, let me go."

"You only had to ask," she complied. "I didn't hurt you, did I?"

"No, Barbarian," — an old joke.

"How have you been, Lady?"

"Fine, and you?" Now we were civilized.

"I would be fine except you never visit me. D.C. isn't far from New York, so why won't you come up?" Barbara asked.

"I hate New York."

She pouted, "Oh, you wouldn't hate it if I showed you around."

"Barbara, you can always visit me. Maryland isn't far, you know."

"I always come to you."

And we were back where we had started. Lea Walsh found us thus. Let me give you the abbreviated history: Lea and Jody were friends, Jody and Barbara were friends, Barbara and Jen were lovers, Jen and Lea were best friends, Lea hated Barbara. Got it?

"Lea, how are you?" Barbara did not extend a hand.

77

"Fine, Barbara. Jody Cross, good to see you, woman!" Of course, we hugged as Barbara looked on impassively.

"Lea, let me tell you right now I don't need no insurance."

She howled at that. "And let me tell you I don't need no muscle fiber analysis. Let me catch you later when we can chat." With that she took off, an intended slight to Barbara.

I turned to give Barbara a rueful look.

"Lea blames me for Jen." Barbara's eyes followed her across the floor.

"Where is Jen? I haven't seen her in years."

Barbara looked at me now. "You, Lea, me and Jen. Or was it you, me, Jen and Lea?"

"I never stepped between you and Jen."

"No, you never did, damn it."

It was 20 years ago, and we were sitting in Mrs. Logan's history class on a warm sunny April day. Barbara and I regarded each other with sleepy amusement. Barbara always wore several bracelets. She took one off and held it out to me. I took it. The bracelet was gold-plated, with an intricate inlaid pattern. I put it on and watched the sunlight caress it. Then I took it off to give it back.

"It's very pretty, Barb."

"It's for you, Jody." She smiled confidently.

"What?"

"I want you to keep it."

"I can't keep this, Barb; it belongs to you."

"Jody, can't I give you my bracelet to wear?"

I thought about Jen, Barb's inseparable familiar of four years. Jen was my friend, too. "Barbara, I'm sorry. I can't take it."

Barbara gave me such a reproachful look as she took the golden band. I wouldn't look at her for the rest of the class.

"No, you never did," Barbara repeated thoughtfully. She took a deep breath and said, "Jen lives in Hawaii. She's so fried from drugs that she qualifies for disability. She has a court-appointed guardian who cashes her checks, presumably to handle Jen's finances." Barbara's eyes never left my face.

"Am I shocked? It's a wonder we all didn't fry. Remember the

78

things we did, what we all tried at least twice? Why didn't more of us fall?"

"Jen started falling in '82 when I moved to New York and my grad program."

"Jen stayed behind."

"Oh, yes."

"Barbara, I'm only an exercise physiologist, but it ain't your fault. You had to go, I had to go, we all had to move on. Oh girl, those were the days. Weed couldn't kill you like crack. The worst thing sex could do was get you pregnant."

"Or give you VD."

"Yeah, but no one died. Life was good and wild and safe."

Barbara smiled. "I'm safe."

"You were never safe, Barbara."

"Well then, I'm good and wild," she murmured as she stepped to me.

I held my ground against her advance.

"Class of 1976, please be seated. Dinner will be served!" Anita's voice rang out.

Barbara took my hand. "Sit with me."

We joined Abby, Cheryl, Sally Wayne and her husband. Sally was overawed with Barbara. She showered praise on Barbara, who responded in a politely humble way. As I ate and chatted with Abby and Cheryl, I became aware of Barbara reaching over to touch my hand, my wrist, my arm every now and then. This was new, as she was never touchy-feely, unless she was pinning me. When I ignored her, she leaned over to say,

"I love what you're doing to me."

"I'm ignoring you!" I exclaimed, stuffing chicken into my mouth.

"Yes, but you always have and I know it means you care."

"For a shrink, you're pretty silly." I speared a carrot.

Barbara stopped my wrist. "I don't want to be your shrink, Jody."

Abby interjected, "Hey, you two keep it light. I'm trying to eat."

I turned from Barbara and engaged in small talk with the other women at the table. Barbara, after slowly releasing my wrist, chatted merrily away as well. We sat through the obligatory speeches from school officials. We applauded our alumnae reps, especially Anita. None too soon, the formalities were over and the music started. The deejay played a mix of hits from '76 and '96. I liked it, and so did Barbara.

"Dance with me, Jody Cross." Barbara stood up smiling, hand outstretched.

"Barbara..." I looked at the dance floor where our classmates and their men were prancing.

"Afraid of what people will think?" Mocking me.

I didn't answer her; I was afraid to.

"They're not thinking about us; not now, not 20 years ago." She paid no heed to my raised eyebrow as she rushed on, touching my hand. "Why do you always put other peoples' feelings ahead of mine? I hate that, but I love you." She shook her head, then went on. "You know, Jody, I can charm most people, but not you. I guess you were sent to keep me humble."

"Obviously it hasn't worked."

Barbara's eyes never left my face as she sank on bended knee. "You think not? Dance with me, Jody Cross." Hard to separate the command from the plea.

"If only to get you off the floor." I stood up and headed for the dance floor, without waiting for her to get to her feet.

The deejay thankfully played fast music. Barbara had this huge smile on her face as we danced. My heart stopped pounding as the songs went on. I was enjoying myself a bit. A few of my classmates and their husbands glanced our way and that was all.

Barbara leaned in to say, "See? No one cares. No one but me." Her hand lingered on my waist. I smiled and danced away a bit but she closed the distance. We repeated this a few times before I gave in and held my ground. Barbara was made glad by this. She invented things to say just so she could lean closer to my smiling face.

"You look so happy when you dance, in a skittish sort of way," Barbara teased, and brushed my waist for the hundredth time.

"Why shouldn't I be happy when I'm dancing with the prettiest woman here?" I replied without returning her touch.

Her face lit up. "Jody, that is easily the nicest thing you've ever said to me!" Her hands strayed over my shoulders, down my arms, my hips.

I looked at her then. "Barbara, you never needed me to tell you anything."

"Maybe not, but I <u>wanted</u> you .... to." Her face was very close to my ear now, her hands touching me again. "Why didn't you ever want to be with me?"

"You were with everyone else: Jen, Richard ... what would I be? Just another conquest for Barbara Sanders."

Barbara regarded me with something less than innocence. "It's not always so bad to be a conquest, you know."

I had no answer for that, so we danced. The deejay was playing "Celebration." Even though this is a fast song, Barbara danced as if it were much slower. She moved closer and closer to me. Touching me and not touching. I retreated, she faithfully followed — smiling.

I stopped, shaking my head. "Barbara, you're driving me crazy."

She too stood still. She grasped my shoulders and said, "I <u>want</u> to drive you crazy, Jody."

It was too much. I stared at her for an instant and then I was gone. I walked straight out the hall into the lobby, out the front door, and into the October night. Calming down, cooling off. Time to face the facts: Barbara and I had always been attracted to one another. When we were girls there was always someone in the way. Barbara was right, I had always weighed her against others and she had always come up short. Maybe I had, too. Barbara excited me, scared me and I did want her that night as she wanted me.

When I returned to the banquet hall, Barbara was standing with a cluster of alums. She immediately came to me.

I met her gaze. "Yes."

"Yes?" She gave me her most radiant smile. Barbara was very close to me now. "Let's go to my room."

Never did take leave of my friends. I followed Barbara into her hotel room. It was a hotel room much like any other: plush carpet, low dresser, color TV, king-sized bed. I walked over to the TV and picked up the cable movie guide. Barbara reclined on the bed, watching me.

"Hey Barbarian, we can watch Sister Act II. I missed it when it came out."

She shook her head as she stood up. "And you're going to miss it again, Jody." She took the movie guide from my hand and threw it to the floor. "We don't sublimate here."

Barbara's arms engulfed me. I melted into her embrace because it was so familiar to me. All those lifesaving drills. She kissed my neck, my ears, my face. By the time she kissed my mouth I could barely stand. But stand I did; I surprised myself. I ran my hands up Barbara's thighs, rustling that pleated skirt. I freed her blouse and let my hands run over her skin. Barbara kissed me harder when I brushed the front of her bra and found her nipples. That blouse came off and ended up on the floor. I pulled Barbara down to me and gave her little bites. My hands coursed down and plunged inside her skirt.

"I want to make love to you," I told Barbara.

She regarded me with eyes aglow. "Suppose I want to make love to you?"

"Wait your turn." I pushed her onto the bed. Barbara rolled on top of me. I let her so I could unzip her skirt and unsnap her bra. We were very warm now, so we stripped out of our clothes. Somehow, I made Barbara lie back. It wasn't easy; Lord she was strong! I smiled down on her,

"Girlfriend, you've got me now."

"No, Lady, you've got me."

I laughed softly as I kissed her breasts — so soft and full! Her stomach was salty and bronze. I settled down between her thighs and felt her shudder just a bit. I wasn't nervous, but I was excited. I showed Barbara just how excited I was. Her hands were strong yet gentle on my face. Her hips rose to meet me, those legs crushed me. I held on to her as she rocked. She moaned and muttered things I couldn't hear. Without warning, she bucked me in the air. I was airborne when she yanked me up and held me to her chest. She rolled on top of me and purposefully ground away on my leg. I helped as best I could. Barbara's teeth were on me now, her breath ragged between thrusts and bites. All at once, she cried out and lay still upon me. I just held her; I could do little else.

In the morning we were all at the Class of '76 Brunch held at the hotel.

82

"What happened to you last night, Cross?" Abby asked.

"Oh, you know, Abby, things come up. Did I miss anything?"

Abby eyed me and Barbara. "No ... and neither do I, Ladies."

I kept a straight face somehow. Barbara laughed.

"So now will you come visit me in New York? We could have a good time, Girl."

"You could visit me. Amtrak runs both ways, you know."

Barbara leaned in to say, "I <u>will</u> visit in the suburbs and you will come to the city, just give me the word."

"So you can clear out your New York ladies?" I asked.

She shook that off. "False jealousy. We go back 20 years, Jody. You give me the word and my place is yours. And you will see me in the land of Mary, so tell her to get when I show."

"Hmm! Such talk from the good Dr. Sanders!" This was the Barbara I liked: selfish, demanding, a little spoiled, breathtaking.

"Are we still friends?" she asked, playing with her eggs.

This time I took her hand and told her, "Always and forever."

Cleo's Gone
by Gwendolyn Bikis

I'm just getting ready to wash my white school blouse when the phone rings.

"Baby sister. What's shakin'?" It's Marla, calling from Charlotte. From the Girls' Club, no doubt, she's talking so streetlike.

"Nothin' doin'," I reply. "You coming home this weekend?"

"I just might. But that sure isn't the reason I'm calling. I just got a call, long distance. From Cleo."

I feel my breath leave me. Already I'm certain this isn't going to be real good.

"She asked me to send her some math books." A pause. "Tammy? She called me from the Wake County Jail. She's 'up against a li'l charge' is all she'll tell me. And she's not sounding too proud of whatever it is she's been charged with *this* time."

I can see the loose little shrug that Cleo'd give, acting cool and shucking, all the way into .. Into prison, this time. Soon as I think it, I know it, know it from the trembling of my voice: "Aah, Maarla —"

Cleo's gone, gone for sure now. Gone for good.

* * * * *

Cleo was Marla's Little Sister, adopted as soon as I went off to college (as soon as I "deserted the mother bosom for the devil white world," as Marla insisted on putting it). I think that I was supposed to be jealous, now that Marla had a substitute, but I was the one who ended up getting that laugh. And Marla was the one who insisted on my meeting Cleo, a fact that I have many times reminded her of.

"I'm working on getting her off the street," Marla had explained to me, on our way over to the Morningside projects across the way from the Girls' Club. "If I can keep her eye on the basketball, I'll be ready to get her back into a school, and get her learning how to read and write, so she'll have something to fall back on besides her shady-side companions."

85

We were walking along the littered sidewalk between two buildings as bare and plain as the brick box my sister Ruthanna stays in, up in Baltimore. Baltimore or Charlotte, it didn't make one difference: both projects seemed alike: ugly, dirty, and way too noisy.

We'd come up on a fence around a weedy asphalt courtyard where bunches of people were smoking and drinking, with a radio playing outside a window:

Hey, some people are made of plastic—
You know, some people are made of wood...

"Cleo's pretty tough," Marla whispered, "so don't be scared, now." She cupped her hands around her mouth and called toward the courtyard: "Cleo Timmons."

"Yo, sistah." Was Cleo playing, or was that the way she really talked? (Would she be angry to know that was my first thought on her "style"?)

From the radio, the song played on:

But, baby, I'm for real —
I'm as real as real can be ...

Cleo, as you first looked to me — leaning back on that fence, your elbows hooked behind the metal posts, looking long and tall and untouchable, in shades and leather jacket and tight black jeans, with black suede tennis shoes on. Your hair grease sparkled in the sun, your hair trailing down below your turned-up jacket collar. You looked tough, all right — although I wasn't scared.

If what you're looking for is good loving,
Then whatchya see is whatchya get ...

Marla had taken me by the hand. "I want you to meet my baby sister. Tammy."

Cleo leaned back even farther and lifted her shades. What was it? I'd never before *felt* any woman's eyes move over my body the way that Cleo's were. Then she smiled, so wide and free I

86

saw right away the little gap between her two front teeth. "Yo, baby sistah. I'm Marla's Little Sister." She smiled wider, then dropped her shades back down as though she weren't yet ready for me to see her.

I got to say it again:
Whatchya see, baby, is what you get ...

But I hadn't really *met* Cleo till I saw her play, saw her legs and arms as long as licorice sticks, licorice so whiplike she nipped the ball out of the other players' fingers, snapped and plucked the rebounds before they hit the blackboard, jumped so quick it seemed there were springs in her knees. Cleo was just a bit darker than me, and built wiry, all tight and smooth at once. If I were to sculpt her, I'd do it all in wire, but no sculpture I could create would ever do her justice. Because Cleo *moved* like silk sliding through water.

Man, oh man, when I think of how gone I was over that girl ... from the early spring of those months I stayed with Marla, managing her team, until the July day she made me leave, I had one hopeless schoolgirl crush. I'd sit on the sidelines making like my own Girls' Club cheerleading squad, until everybody started to see who I was really cheering for. And the thing was, Cleo didn't need any more cheering.

"F that 'everybody's a star' stuff. I'm the only star on this team." And she'd thump her ball a couple of times off the locker room bench, as if to punch the point home. After she was given her Most Valuable Player trophy, every kid on the block wanted Cleo's autograph. I remember her smiling in a mob of kids, her face still shining with sweat, her royal red jacket snapped closed over her shoulders, signing scrap after scrap of paper. "Good luck. Signed C.L."; "Happy baskets, signed C.L." Even though she couldn't write very well (the ink pen looked funny, bobbling loosely in her fingers), she grinned through every minute of it. "That might be the only time you'll see Cleo happy to be holding a pen," Marla grumbled. Sometimes she'd get so discouraged with her other Little Sister.

Like anyone else with an awkward name, Cleo always had plenty of nicknames — C.L., Likorish, Lik-Stick Timmons — all

87

of them hiding the name of — Cleotha. Cleo hated Cleotha, hated it with a red-eyed passion, hated it like she hated being stepped on. Cleotha reminded her of a "dumpty country girl with glasses," a girl who'd be afraid of someone like Cleo, so afraid that she'd give up all her lunch money, let herself be kissed, then offer over her sandwich.

"I beat plenty of kids up for food when I was a child," Cleo bragged. "I just had to, they was being so greedy. It ain't *polite* to eat in front of folks who just ain't got. It ain't right, so I had to start on them." Cleo rubbed her fist in the palm of her hand and shook her head in sadness that at least looked real.

"I would have given you some," I recall my saying.

"You would have given me *all*, baby." She smiled then, showing off the squareness of her chin.

Cleo is an Aries, like me: sometimes we're so selfish, we don't even know we're being it. Or so Marla says. (I suppose I should have *offered* Cleo all of my sandwich. Marla would have.) Even so, I do believe that Cleo's a whole lot more selfish than me. *I* would think twice about kissing someone, especially some other girl — even more, some other girl who, most likely, would not want it — but Cleo claimed that she only picked the girls who'd want it. After she picked me, and after she kissed me, she told me, "I knew you'd like it, once I did it, so I just went ahead and did." And that smile again: flashing, then closing, like the quick white glint of a pocketknife.

Cleo thought she was smooth, but she sure had one quick attitude. Let someone step on her toes wrong (in a basketball game, for goodness' sake!) and Cleo'd go off. I remember seeing tears in her eyes one time, she was so hurt that someone had made her so red-hot mad. I can still see the way she got, cutting her eyes and snarling about "someone." That time, I think, "someone" had draped Cleo's jacket over their own "stinkin', sweatin' shoulders." By mistake, but you sure couldn't tell Cleo that, just like you couldn't tell her that this wasn't the training school, where everyone just naturally stole from her, the young-est and the skinniest of all.

That's how I knew, the game she let me wear her jacket for a whole entire two quarters, that Cleo really thought of me as "her girl."

After that game, after everyone was gone, with the showers dripping and me innocently picking up the dirty towels, Cleo backed me up against the lockers, and her mouth was spicy with the taste of Good 'n' Plenty. I knew, after that day, that it was only a matter of time before I'd be back on the bus toward Alma.

* * * * *

Cleo ... your sleek legs flying, your lanky muscles stretching tight the stripes around your socks, around the hems of your red silk, real tight basketball shorts...

Her jump shots were so smooth she could have been diving up through water, and watching her make them put me in the shivers, as though she were sliding, silkenly, all along the most secret of my places. She'd bounce and flick that ball around a helpless tangle of legs and arms that hopelessly tried to stop her. One time, she dribbled the ball right out of "some chick's" fingers, then, darting and springing around her, bounced the ball — I swear — right through the girl's outspread legs, catching it off the bounce before the poor girl even had the chance to think of turning around. "Smooth black is hard to attack" was Cleo's motto for her playing style, but it applied as well to all her other ways, on all her other days, in all the other places.

"Cleo's Back," said the front of her favorite black sweatshirt, in bright pink letters. "Cleo's Gone," said the other side. "Slick" was the word she'd use to describe herself, because like every true Player, Cleo had two sides: street side and court side. On the court, Cleo most liked to wear her lucky black canvas hightops, but coming in off the street, she always wore new suede or leather tennis shoes, and she cussed if someone so much as scuffed them, and fussed when someone (like Marla) merely asked her where she'd gotten them from.

"Because she knew I was actually asking her where did she get the wherewithal to get them from."

Everybody knew that Cleo had absolutely no visible means, other than hanging around the littered, rotten-smelling courtyard of the M.C. Morningside Homes, hanging out supposedly empty-handed.

89

"But you never can tell what-all I got in my socks or my secret pockets," she bragged.

I'd gone over to the Morningside to look for her, that last morning I spent with her ("You have exactly twenty minutes to go and say good-bye to her," Marla said, and tapped her wrist-watch, and I knew she thought she was being fair to give me that), but I didn't have to look far. Cleo was waiting for me in the stairwell of her building, on a step with her ball in her hand.

"Hi, baby sis." She stood and flicked her leg muscles. And she smiled, her tongue pressed teasingly to the gap between her teeth.

"Hey, Likorish," I said, in a voice thick with all my misery.

"Ah, don't be taking it that way." She reached for my hand and pulled me toward her. Her ball had dribbled away into a corner. "Just 'cause big sis don't want you hanging out with big old bad-ass me no more."

"I couldn't give a care *what* Marla wants," I decided out loud. Now, what did I do that for, I remember thinking, because what Cleo did then was press her bare lanky leg into my — you know. My breath froze: what was she doing to me? I fell helplessly into a shiver.

Her tongue was on my lips, and she was pressing me closer and moving her kissing to my cheek, my chin, all down my neck. All I could do was close my eyes and try very hard not to make a noise. Where in the world was Marla when I needed her?

"You have such a long, long neck," she was crooning, and what did I do but smile and stretch it longer for more kisses? Both her hands were holding tight to my behind, so I couldn't get away. I reached for her own round, high-riding ... "Hey, girl!" And she pulled back from me, so suddenlike she scared me, and slapped my wrists away.

"What, Cleo?" I almost felt like crying.

"Let's go upstairs," she whispered, hotly, in my ear, with her hands holding mine behind me.

Feeling shamed and tough and sneaky, I crept up her four flights right behind her. "Sssh." Cleo put her finger to her mouth as she quietly opened her apartment's door. "Auntie-dear is sleeping." We slipped inside, past a darkened living room-kitchenette, on into Cleo's bedroom, where she latched the door.

I looked around, a little desperately, because there certainly
wasn't much in that little bedroom to offer any distraction, or
even conversation: just a very neat bureau with her trophy on it,
a poster of a long, tall player with his arm arched ready to sink a
basket, and a made-up bed with her tennis shoes — all eight
pairs — neatly lined up under it. Cleo grinned, noticing, of
course, where I was looking. "I'll be your good girl if you'll put
your shoes underneath my bed," she sang. She was leading me
right to it, sliding her hand along her pillow. "I want to rub your
tummy till your cherry turns bright red." By now her hand was
all up under my blouse, her fingers gently pinching the sweet-
meat of my belly, creeping down toward my zipper.

Next I knew, I was on my back, barefooted, with my skirt off
and Cleo's fingers inching up my thigh, close to my...

"M-a-arla," I wanted to yell. Why didn't I?

She began massaging me down there, with the strong com-
manding palm of her hand, the whole while singing in my ear:
"Won't your sister be disgusted, when she see your cherry
busted?" I might've tried to reply, or wanted to wiggle away, but
I couldn't hardly, because she was holding me down and covering my mouth with her lips, her kiss, and one of her long, sleek
legs was sliding up between mine, so that my belly had begun to
shake. Escape was even harder when she slipped her fingers
under my panties. "Take yo' drawers off, sugar babe?"

Well, what could I do? I let her take my panties off. "Ride me,
baby," she begged me, her breath hot, almost sobbing. "Wrap 'em
all around me." Then she was sliding and gliding all over me,
until I caught her rhythm deep down inside my middle, all
through my shivering secret places.

"Oooh." My eyes popped open when she put her fingers there,
pumping them in and out as I felt myself foam like clabber and
tighten around her. And she pulled me up tight, churning in and
out until my hips rocked the bed so hard, so steady, that its
springs began to sing. Cleo was laughing as I thrashed and bit
the pillow; she was laughing and kissing me rashly around my
face. "You really like that, huh, baby, huh?" I was swooning,
seeing nothing but velvet wings brushing their black tips across
the midnight sky. I couldn't even moan, she had my mouth so
covered, my lips and tongue so tightly wrapped and pressed in

hers.

"Oh, Tammy, that's some sweet—" and she used that *p* word, that nasty, sticky-sweet word. Evil, coming from a street curb, but here just soft and tender, the way I'd never heard it. I groaned and pushed myself up tighter.

"Cleo!" Cleo's auntie's voice, just the other side of the door. Cleo's hand came away from me so fast I collapsed back onto the bed.

"Ma'am?"

"It's someone here to see you."

She stood up, wiped her fingers on her bedspread. "We'd best get you redressed, baby sis. It's probably big sis now."

Just like Marla, always right on time but never coming right when I wanted her. Marla had her hand propped up on her hip, and her foot tapped impatiently while I asked aunt for an ink pen and paper so that I could at least get Cleo's address.

"I'll write," I promised Cleo's laughing eyes, and hugged her oh-so-stiffly. "Time to go, Tammy" was all that Marla said, and I could tell by the tightness of her lips and the way she wouldn't even look at Cleo, or my very wrinkled blouse, that she knew.

Outside, I felt obliged to explain: "We was just —"

"Tamara, you know, I ain't even gon' ask." I could tell how upset she was by her grammatical slip.

"It wasn't anything, Marla."

"I am sure it wasn't. I am sure she just led you up there, like Mary had a little innocent lamb."

And you know, to this day that is probably what Marla is telling herself.

I throbbed the whole ride home, wriggling restlessly in my bus seat just at the thought of Cleo's fingers there inside me. Damn Marla, damn, I swore, squirming hooked through the middle on a stiff velvet rope. I would have sworn even harder if I'd known that would be the last time I'd ever see Cleo. A couple of months after Marla sent me away, Cleo disappeared anyway, and nobody that Marla asked was telling where to.

Coming Out Story
by Michele Hunter

The morning of the New Year, Lone Pony Movers arrived at my door. My girlfriend Eve was helping me load the truck with the one mover, Jeff, who was complaining about how much stuff I had. His rickety van carried us from Jamaica Plain to Cambridge. On the ride, Jeff and Eve talked about their hometowns in Massachusetts. He had grown up and was still living in Somerville, a town situated next to Cambridge. Eve grew up in Worcester, a small working class town 40 miles outside of Boston.

Unlike Jeff, Eve didn't stick around to work in the area to support an unemployed husband and several god-fearing children. She had plans to be much more than that. Her adoptive parents, teachers at the local and mostly white prep school she attended, sent her to Oberlin College. And from there, she set her sights on a career that would keep her out of the ghetto she believed could be her destiny.

Like me, Eve is biracial. Her white mother fell in love with a black man in college who wouldn't support her child, so she was forced to give it up. The town of Worcester was up in arms about a white family adopting a little brown baby, but the Archer family stuck to its religious and humanitarian convictions and kept little Eve 'til she was grown.

A year before the move, when I met Eve at an office job I had in New York City, I was intrigued because I had an inkling about her heritage. I didn't know how to approach her just for that reason ("hey you! are you biracial? so am I!"). No, I figured, that wouldn't be "sophisticated" enough — especially in New York City, where you had to *work* at getting to know people. So I tried something that I had been asked in college by a woman who wanted the same information from me, "So, what do you do to your hair?"

Immediately, Eve was impressed that I should take notice of her appearance — let alone her beauty secrets. As it turned out, she had never figured out how exactly to take care of her hair, but she confided in me about what secrets she did have. "I buy this stuff up in Harlem..." Shortly after, she brought it to work just to show me and when I told her I didn't think I could find anything like that in Park Slope, Brooklyn, she said she would get some for me.

Well, the hair question worked. Just like the woman I met in college, Eve and I were talking and quickly became friends. Since we were about the same age and had both been out of college for a short time, we had a lot to talk about. I was living with my boyfriend at the time and she was closeted at the office, so we both got to know each other as straight women.

I confided to Eve all of my deepest secrets, like the fact that I was applying to graduate school and didn't plan to stick around the office forever. We exchanged gossip about our co-workers and the office politics. Since she and I had both majored in Women's Studies, we also spent considerable time discussing our ideas and experiences with feminism. Eve took an interest in my academic plans and was one of the first to know when I received my rejection letters. She was unmistakably impressed when I told her that I had been accepted by Harvard. In fact, she was probably seduced by it.

Eve and I became so close that I would miss her when I didn't go to work. One day, when I was at home from work, I called her.

"You called the office just to talk to me?"

"Yeah, well I wanted to talk to you. I missed talking to you." My face and ears had flushed. I didn't exactly know what was happening to me, but I suddenly felt really embarrassed.

"Well, I'm glad you called to talk to me. I missed talking to you, too," she said with a smile in her voice.

We said our goodbyes and I felt like I wasn't sure what I had just done.

* * * * *

A couple of days later, I managed to get tickets to see Prince that same night at Radio City Music Hall. I invited Eve and my friend Donna, who both gladly accepted. This was already becoming a very special day for me, because Prince was my one and only favorite recording artist. It had been years since I had been able to see him in concert.

I met Eve and Donna at the concert and shared the good news with them that I'd received mail from Harvard that afternoon: I'd been awarded a full scholarship. We celebrated to the live music and had the most fun I'd had in a long while. At this point, I'd known Eve for less than a month. Since we decided that it was just too late for me to go all the way home to Brooklyn (even though I'd done it many times before), Eve invited me over to her apartment on 125th Street and Broadway to stay the night. On the train ride, she began to get noticeably uncomfortable. Before I could ask her what was wrong, she said,

"Now, when we get to my apartment, you're going to see a lot of ... umm ... pornography."

"What do you mean?"

"Well, you know, I have posters on the wall and stuff."

"Oh." So what? I wondered, maybe she thinks I'm a prude. "Porn doesn't bother me," I said, hoping to make her feel less concern. Then, she announced,

"I'm queer."

"What?"

"I'm queer, I'm a lesbian." She didn't know where to look. As she spoke to me, her forearms were sitting on her thighs and her hands were in a tense lock.

How did I take it? I was excited and intimidated. What had I gotten myself into? I wondered, staying over at a bona fide lesbian's house. Boy, was I in for something special. The elated, celebratory feeling from the evening was still fluttering in my heart. I said, "Well, I figured you were at least bisexual," trying to keep my cool.

"What do you mean by 'at least bisexual'? How could you tell?"

"Things you said. Like, when you laughed for a whole fifteen minutes over that mannequin in the window by the office be-cause you could see her nipples. You just stood there pointing and saying over and over, 'You can see her actual nipples! Look! You can see her hard nipples!' And that time when we were eating lunch and you were looking at that black woman and you said, 'She's hot.'"

95

"You caught that? You remember when I said that?" She looked down as I confirmed that yes, I did remember it very well. "That was a major slip," she said. "You weren't s'posed to hear me say that." We both laughed out loud.

Eve was gentle with me when we got to her house. We spent the night talking about my feelings about my sexuality while she listened supportively. We didn't get to sleep until about 4:30 in the morning. Being in the twin size loft bed with her was just too exciting.

Her roommate lent me a dress for work and Eve and I pretended that we were coming to work from our respective homes. On just three hours of sleep, it was a long, long day.

* * * * *

Jeff brought us to the grey three-story house on Beacon Street in less than a half hour. I was so excited to move so much closer to school. No more midnight bus rides. I ran my things up and down the stairs. As soon as all of the boxes were settled, Eve and I noticed that the heat didn't work. In fact, there was no heat. I found a small space heater in my new bedroom and an electric blanket. Together, Eve and I devised ways to keep warm...

When we went out to get breakfast down the street, Eve wouldn't hold my hand. While we sat in the coffee shop, she refused me, again. "What's the matter?"

"It's not safe."

"What are you talking about? It's mostly students who live here and a lot of lesbians — they don't care."

"Well, I don't feel safe."

Eve didn't usually feel "safe," as she called it. The only time when PDA was acceptable with her was during Pride in Washington, D.C., and occasionally in Jamaica Plain, which was known for having a large lesbian population. At first, I trusted that it was thoughtless to make yourself a visible target, as she put it, but after a while, I started to feel utterly rejected.

"This isn't just about safety, Eve. This is about being affectionate and expressing love. You never touch me, anymore."

It was true. We had spent our Christmas vacation in a lesbian guesthouse and Eve felt conflicted about being sexual with me. During the winter holidays, Eve was visiting me from New York for an entire two weeks and every minute counted. It was devastating to me that she wouldn't touch me.

"We only had sex twice this whole vacation."

"You make everything sound so crude, Michele. So what if we only had sex twice? What's wrong with that?"

"We used to have sex several times a day, don't you remember? What the fuck happened?" Eve had a point that I didn't know how to be tactful when we talked about sex, but I had reached an insurmountable level of frustration. We argued until her ride back to New York came, never really making up.

Despite the cold, I loved living closer to campus. Finals were starting and I especially needed access to the library at all hours to work on my papers. I turned in my first paper on time and stayed home that night relaxing. Eve called me shortly afterwards. We had a nice conversation until she told me that she had a crush on someone — a man.

"What? Who is it?" I said in total disbelief.

"This guy I met through work."

"Is it someone you're working with now?"

"No, I met him at a meeting outside of the office."

Suddenly all of her probing about heterosexual sex came to mind. "So tell me how straight people position themselves, Michele. Are there different positions?" and so on. Like a fool, I willingly gave her a tour of all that I knew at 24. She readily and eagerly took note of everything I taught her. I thought it was just a game she liked to play with me, to tease me about being straight and sleeping with men, but now I was feeling scared.

"If you won't tell me who he is, then will you tell me how you're going to deal with your feelings?"

"I don't know. I don't know what to do. I really like him."

When we hung up, I felt numb.

* * * * *

A few nights after we went to see Prince and Eve came out to me, we had dinner together in the Village. We talked and talked

97

for three hours like two people on their first date, or maybe their third. There was a familiarity and an ease that I felt with Eve that I hadn't felt with anyone else before. I thought that she understood me better than men, white people *and* black people. The speed at which we found a connection was uncanny.

"A big part of me doesn't want to go home to Brooklyn, Eve," I confided. We were having such a good time, I didn't want it to end when we left the restaurant.

"Do you want to stay over?" she asked me, as casually as she could muster.

"OK," I responded in equal coolness.

We left the restaurant and walked arm in arm to the subway station.

When we got to her apartment, we went to her room and changed into the clothes she had for bed. She got out her nail file and clippers.

"You're going to clip your nails, *now?*" I said naively.

"Yeah, do you want me to cut yours, too?" "Alright." I slid under the covers next to her, watching her carefully cut her nails. She'd said she'd grown her nails in protest and I surely did not know what she'd meant. Mine were already pretty short because I just couldn't stand for them to be very long, anyways. Little did I know that I was ahead of the game.

"Give me your hand." Eve took my right hand and clipped the stubs I had for nails. When she finished my right hand, I took her hand and clipped hers. When I was done, she finished my left hand and started to kiss my fingers. I took her hand and kissed hers back. Then Eve and I moved closer to one another and kissed each other on the lips.

I can't describe what happened that night because I would be giving away the only thing I really had with Eve — my first time.

* * * * *

A few months later, I made Eve breakfast in bed in my Brooklyn apartment. I brought the platter of food to bed, laid it under a thick dishtowel and pleasantly watched Eve's eyes open

98

wide with surprise. We ate and watched television together, snuggling, looking at the images, half-listening to the senseless conversations and stories in my king size bed.

I began to kiss her on the ear, then the neck. I held her chin in my hands and gave her mouth to mine, kissing her so gently. Then I stopped. She looked into my eyes and said, "Fuck me..."

Later, when we looked at the sheets, she noticed that I was bleeding. She hadn't cut her nails for a long time and had probably scratched my insides. I slowly crept to the bathroom, sat on the toilet and watched the blood pour out of me. It wouldn't stop, no matter how calm I tried to be, no matter how much I was freaking out inside. I was so terrified that something was wrong with me. I thought of the stories young women told in horror about the first time their periods came. When they looked down and saw so much blood coming from the most sensitive part of their bodies, and the feelings of fear, worry and panic that came with the unknown and the unexplainable loss of blood.

I tried my best not to panic. Especially when she entered the bathroom and explained to me how common this was in lesbian sex. *How common...*

While she made herself comfortable on the bathroom cabinet, I looked at her long nails and thought about the first time I clipped them for her. When we first slept together and I didn't know what the hell I was doing. All I knew was that I must clip her nails because she had been growing them to protest her celibacy.

Her nails grew beautifully on her. She had long, slim fingers and when her nails grew, they fit like smooth gloves over the ends of her perfect hands. Since that night, her nails had grown much longer than they should have —regardless of her sexual habits.

As I sat on the toilet sporadically checking the basin of water below me and feeling the insides and outsides of my genitals warning me that they weren't going to willingly feel so raw, again, I gazed at Eve, sitting in my bathroom in my pajamas, and felt as though I loved her for caring and hated her for doing this to me.

She told me how irresponsible I was for not seeing a gyne-cologist for five years. My blood dripped into the cold, pink

99

water. She told me she had little tolerance for women who didn't take care of themselves. I felt like an open sore. She then asked me why I hadn't gone to a doctor in so long. I told her about wanting to be perfectly healthy for the doctor, I told her I hated stirrups, I told her all sorts of things. Then she said something about not taking care of myself and I said something about not wanting to take care of my body because I hated my body.

Was I at the point where I was prepared to be so open with her, so vulnerable? I wasn't sure, but I almost couldn't help myself.

* * * * *

A few days after Eve told me that she was interested in a guy, I decided that it wasn't a good idea for her to come to visit me in Cambridge for the weekend. But that Saturday, an electrical fire destroyed my home and guess who showed up?

"She took the first train to Boston she could get to when she heard your message about the fire," her roommate said. "She'll be there around 11 tonight."

While she was in town, Eve gave me everything I needed: a place to stay, a strong voice with which to deal with the attorneys, a shoulder to cry on, and every second of her time. Day and night, night and day, Eve was there for me, doing everything she thought I needed to have done — and I let her. But, she still wouldn't touch me in public and her feelings for the guy hadn't changed.

* * * * *

I lost Eve shortly after I lost my home. After Eve, there really was no turning back for me. I had experienced a lifestyle that I could not and finally would not ever give up. So, while she explored the possibility of being with a man in New York, I read everything I could get my hands on about lesbian identity and introduced myself to as many lesbians and gay men as possible. "How do I be a lesbian without a girlfriend?" I asked everyone.

100

"Just be yourself," I was told.

Coming out means coming alive. Experience has taught me that no one can give you what you can give yourself — coming out is one of those things.

From a Lesbian Womb Into a Lesbian World: Coming Out
by Laura Irene Wayne

Coming out: "to move toward a place, a point, to arrive, to reach a condition, to become visible or revealed or known." (Oxford Dictionary)

As far as I can remember, I have always been out and treated as out. It is like I was born with a black triangle on my forehead, or that gaydar really works. It seemed everyone knew. I had no need or want to ever hide it. So the only coming out I can remember is swimming and coming out of mother's womb with labrys* in hand and bellowing one hell of an Amazon battle cry. It was as if when I was being conceived, a discussion of my gender took place. One with the Lesbian Goddess of Sexuality and my Fairy Dyke Mother (a butch-femme sistah). Their praying and influence over the chromosomes determined my lesbian, dyke, butch, femme, attitude, personality, spirit and soul. They happily imprinted the word Lesbian in my head, my heart and on my birth certificate.

Perhaps, though, my sexuality could've been determined by my mother, who was once a Lesbian. A Lesbian who tried to cure herself by having 12 children, only to birth two lesbians, two bisexuals and eight others. My mother probably returned to her re-occurring dreams, her fantasies of her unforgotten wonderful Lesbian lifestyle, lusting after Womyn during my conception and/or when she carried me for nine months.

Whatever the case may be, I came from a Lesbian womb into a Lesbian World. My paths were lined with friends, family, potlucks, parades, protests, festivals, triangles giving me directions and rainbow flags flying, celebrating, empowering and affirming me.

Maybe that is why I knew closets were only for clothes and I only stored my black leather jacket and my collection of Doc Martens in them.

Maybe I am an out Lesbian because of my strong Amazon body, my love for sports, for Womyn, my aggressive intelligent sense of self, my ability to know and to go after what I want and

103

not conform.

Maybe I was accepted as a Lesbian because of the way I look and think.

Maybe I accepted Lesbianism because of its politics on loving, protecting, celebrating and empowering Womyn, or just maybe we are one and the same.

Maybe I am an out Lesbian because of my strong, beautiful, intelligent, visible Gay brothers and Lesbian sistahs from past to present. Who were out, and are out there as mentors.

Maybe I am an out Lesbian because I take pride in uniqueness and myself. I am proud to be selected as one of the few, those exceptionally special people.

Maybe it's because I am able to celebrate and embrace difference.

However or whatever the case may be, I am a Lesbian because I was chosen, but I am an out African-American Lesbian Feminist, Artist, Poet and Activist because I know of its importance and I choose to be.

---

* labrys: A double-bladed ax used ceremonially by the ancient Amazonian goddess, and adopted by present-day lesbians as a reminiscent symbol of the all-female society of Lesbos, according to *The Woman's Encyclopedia of Myths and Secrets* by Barbara G. Walker.

Halfway Home: Interview with Katherine James
by Denise Moore

[Katherine James is a pseudonym for a woman who works as support personnel in the music industry in Los Angeles.]

Katherine James: Now when I get rich and famous, I don't want to hear this "exclusive interview only here on *ET*" or *Hard Copy,* OK?

Denise Moore: Girl, I ain't gonna remember your name. Don't worry about it, I'm on my way to rich and famous. But I'ma be out when I'm famous. Now, first question: What does it mean to be an out lesbian, to you?

KJ: Damn!

DM: OK, if someone tells you they're out, what do you think they mean?

KJ: It means to me that they let everybody know that they're gay.

DM: Everybody like who?

KJ: Like their jobs, their families... Well, you've met people like that. They're just like, "I'm out." They'll tell anybody, "No, I'm not into you, because I'm gay." If a guy tries to hit on them, they say, "No, I'm gay."

DM: Don't you find that a little interesting? Do you think you should tell everybody you're gay? Do you think you should be out to everybody?
KJ: I know some people that are. They don't care. They don't care. I guess they happen to have jobs where it's not a priority.

DM: To what extent do you consider yourself to be out?

KJ: I would say about halfway.

DM: Out to yourself?

KJ: All the way.

DM: Friends?

KJ: 'Bout halfway.

DM: Family?

KJ: In the closet with the door closed and the light off!

DM: All right! (laughter) You're about right, halfway. The halfway home for lesbians! Now, do you have a significant event or series of events that illustrate what your coming out experience was? What happened to make you think, OK, I'm an out lesbian?

KJ: What happened...?

DM: Did anything happen? Did you tell somebody? Was there a thing that happened that made you feel like you were a lesbian, and that's that? How did you come out to yourself? What made you tell yourself you were a lesbian?

KJ: Well, you know, I've always been attracted to girls, even when I was a little girl. God, this brings back, like, real memories. When I was in seventh grade, I used to have this crush on this girl named Terry, who was in eighth grade, and I just thought Terry was like the cutest thing. Then, I was in eighth grade, and I had this crush on this girl named Angela, and she was in the year under me. And I used to sneak in her homeroom and put love notes in her desk...

DM: Love notes! Girl, you was bold!

KJ: But I didn't put my name on them! I would sign it "Your

Secret Admirer." I would see her and her little friends giggling in the corner with the note. Tee-hee-hee-hee! Like some boy wrote the note, and I'd be like, mm-hmm.

DM: I got your boy for ya...

KJ: So I kind of figured I would grow out of it. How old were you when you were in eighth grade, like 12?

DM: 12, 13.

KJ: Yeah.

DM: What was the girl like, the one who was your first love? What did she look like?

KJ: She was like nobody who I'm attracted to now.

DM: Ooh, she was white!

KJ: (laughter) This was like freshman year in college. She was brown-skinned, had dimples, long hair; she looked cute to me.

DM: What kind of eyes did she have?

KJ: Brown.

DM: Big, little, almond-shaped, big doe eyes... what?

KJ: Just regular eyes!

DM: Regular ol' eyes.

KJ: It wasn't nothing, like, outstanding about her, but to me she just ...

DM: What did she do that attracted you to her?

KJ: I was attracted to her all along. We were in the same sorority;

we pledged together. I always thought she was cute, and umm... one day we went home for spring break or something like that, and she went to this gay club. And she came back to school and was telling me about the club. She was like, "Oh, I went to this club with a friend of mine. The music was pumping, but it was a gay club, so we didn't have anybody to dance with." Then we just started kinda hinting around each other and hinting and saying bullshit and finally we admitted that both of us were gay. It pretty much spiraled.

DM: So there wasn't anything special she did that attracted you? Just knowing that she was gay?

KJ: Yeah, she was, like, the first gay person that I knew.

DM: Were you seduced, or was your first same-sex encounter considered mutual experimentation?

KJ: I would say it was mutual.

DM: Experimentation?

KJ: Well, she had been with a girl before I had, and then it was just like a natural thing, 'cause she was like, "Are you sure you've never been with a girl before?" I said, "No."

DM: Macked it! She was a mack on the first time! So there was no seduction. Well, what happened? How y'all got together? You don't just end up nekkid with somebody!

KJ: Well, you know we used to just mess around in a dorm room, something like that...

DM: ... kissing and stuff like that...

KJ: Yeah. And one night I had spent the night over at her dorm room, and... just messing around. This was the first time. I don't know, I guess I was meant to be gay, 'cause I knew what to do, and I just went for it.

DM: Well, how did it start?

KJ: I guess while we were sleeping in the same bed, and we just started messing around with each other. I don't know, I was fumbling with her underwear, and she took 'em off, and started on me, and I said, "I think you need some help."

DM: Good evening! I gotta try that! OK, are there any particular character, personality traits that attract you to women?

KJ: Character. And I usually like light-skinned women, but I've been trying to see dark-skinned women, enjoy darker women.

DM: Why?

KJ: I don't know. Well, my friends call me color-struck.

DM: Do you like black girls who are feminine, girls who are androgynous or...?

KJ: Femme.

DM: What's femme?

KJ: Give me a girl with pumps.

DM: Mmm, I like them too! Well, what's butch?

KJ: Butches, to me, are those girls that walk around in those suits and Stacey Adams shoes and just think they're a man. Girls that wear boxer shorts and men's socks and just go overboard.

DM: So am I butch or femme?

KJ: I think you're kinda what I am. Neither. Not butch nor femme.

DM: I guess that answers the next question: Do either of these terms describe you? Why or why not? Why are you either not butch or femme? Why don't these terms describe you?

KJ: I guess 'cause I'm in the middle. You know, I'm not, like, all the way, so anti-man that I have to dress like a man. Well, let me take that back. I'm not, like, I want to be a man so much that I have to dress like a man and wear men's clothes and wear suits and ties, shit like that, like some girls do. But then again, I'm not femme. I don't own a dress. I've got one pair of pumps, I've got one suit that has a skirt. The majority of the time, 99 percent of the time, I'll wear slacks.

DM: What was the best thing a lover ever said to you?

KJ: "Can I buy you a car!" No, I guess, "I love you." The first-time "I love you."

DM: How do you feel about men in general?

KJ: I don't dislike men. I'm just not... I was telling a friend of mine, I'm not emotionally attracted to you. Like, I'll see a guy, and if he's cute, I'll give him his props, like, "Oh, he's gorgeous!" But as far as spiritual or emotional ties with men, I don't have them. They bore me.

DM: So if you find a man attractive, it's just aesthetic, or is there some kind of little tingly thing?

KJ: Nah, no tingly, definitely.

DM: Have you ever had a male lover?

KJ: Yeah.

DM: Why?

KJ: Because that's when I was in high school, and that was the thing to do. You just had a boyfriend, somebody to go to the prom with, school dances...

DM: Who knows you're a lesbian?

KJ: A few of my friends. Mostly friends.

DM: Who doesn't know?

KJ: Family.

DM: Why?

KJ: Girl, they would trip out!

DM: My next question is, the title of this book, "Does Your Mother Know?"

KJ: NO! Is your mother gonna know? NO!

DM: We might change it to "Do Yo Mama Know?" I'm still working on that, 'cause I like that title better. And we came up with another one, just, "Ya Mama Know?" (laughter) Do you think it's more difficult to be out in the African-American community?

KJ: I think it is. Because for some reason white America accepts gay people more freely than African-Americans.

DM: Do white Americans accept African-American gay people?

KJ: Straight white Americans or gay white Americans?

DM: Either.

KJ: I think gay white Americans do.

DM: To what extent? What's been your experience? Have you dated a white woman?

KJ: Have I dated a white woman? No. I'm not attracted to white women. I'm not attracted to pink nipples.

DM: Wait a minute! How are you gonna be color-struck and not

111

like a high-yellow woman! I got pink nipples and I know it, OK!

KJ: They ain't that pink, probably, like...!

DM: No, they ain't like that, but you know what I'm saying.

KJ: You all are light, you're not white! A white girl is actually, like, three shades lighter than you!

DM: OK, I got personal, I'm sorry. As an African-American lesbian woman, who would you consider a role model?

KJ: My role model right now is Sylvia Rhone. Do you know who she is?

DM: I'm gonna read about her next week. Go ahead and tell me.

KJ: She's the first woman, black, African-American woman to run a record label. She runs East West Record
DM: What famous or historical figures do you like you?

KJ: None.

DM: None?

KJ. No.

DM: Describe your dream lover. What would she look like? What kind of personality would she have?

KJ: Kind of outgoing, 'cause I'm not really that outgoing. She could bring me out. I'd like her to get along with people, so I could take her to functions. She's gotta be cute, gotta be social...

DM: ... and she's gotta look good in those pumps!

KJ: Back to the pumps!

DM: Anyway... What kind of lover would she be?

KJ: Well, you know there's all kinds of ways to make love. Somebody who'll let me do the freaky shit, 'cause I'm a Scorpio.

DM: Oh, OK; got that freaky thing going. Would you support a lover? Financially?

KJ: If she was trying to do something positive — like if she was in law school or medical school — definitely. Something to better her career. But if she was just sitting at the crib all day watching "All My Children," hell, no!
DM: Would you date a woman with children?

KJ: Yeah, I have. I love kids. Matter of fact, I want to have a kid.

DM: What kind of relationship would you like, in a perfect world? No societal restrictions, no judgement calls...

KJ: Just having people accept gay couples. Being able to just walk downtown with your girlfriend.

DM: Would you want a monogamous relationship?

KJ: Yeah, definitely. There's people dying out there.

DM: Well, in a perfect world there would be no AIDS.

KJ: Oh, we're going all the way there! Oh, so I can sneak out the back door every now and then!

DM: So let me understand. You want a sexual relationship that allows you to experiment outside the relationship.

KJ: Uh-huh. No, I'm joking. Monogamy.

DM: Where would you get money?

KJ: If this was a perfect world, I would own my own record

113

label. I would have that bomb artist pumping out the dope tracks.

DM: What are your specific political concerns?

KJ: Suffice it to say I'm really not an activist. Although I should be more political correct, I'm really not. I support freedom of choice, because we've got too many unwanted kids in the world now. Health care, I think about that a lot.

DM: What do you think about voting in America? How does it affect your life?

KJ: Well, I get out there and vote in major elections, like the presidential campaign. I'm not gonna lie, I don't vote for local stuff, like senator, mayor. Especially since I'm in California.

DM: What are your social concerns?

KJ: I guess it's to get society AIDS-free.

DM: What are your specific economic goals?

KJ: Have you ever heard of this cologne called Bijan? He has a series of billboards all around L.A. There's just him, by himself, with a bottle of cologne, and the billboard says, "I never dreamed I could be this rich." I drive the freeway and I see those billboards, and I say, "Yeah!"

DM: Do you have any children?

KJ: No.

DM: How would you like the children in your life to view your lifestyle?

KJ: I want them to understand. I'm not gonna hide it. 'Cause I think kids can grow up in a healthy environment knowing that their mom was gay.

114

DM: Are there any kids around you now?

KJ: I have a nephew.

DM: How does he view your lifestyle?

KJ: He doesn't know. Neither does my sister.

DM: If you had to give one solid piece of advice to a young black woman questioning her sexuality, what would it be?

KJ: Go for what you feel. Follow your heart. That's what I've learned to do; follow my heart. Not your head; it's your heart.

I Guess I Never Will
by Tonda Clarke

As far back as I can remember, I was a gay girl. As a child,
my family pegged me as a tomboy because my interests were
never captivated by the traditional trappings of girlhood. Every
Christmas, dolls, make-believe makeup kits and Easy Bake
ovens would lie lonely and untouched under the tree. I would
wait patiently for my cousins, all boys, to arrive with the trucks,
trains and Hot Wheels track that I always asked for but never
received.

As I grew older, I did not entertain thoughts of becoming a
woman so that I could marry a man and have children. Instead, I
fantasized about being an explorer uncovering mystical and
ancient treasures from uncharted territories. Momma said that I
would grow out of it. I had no clue as to what she thought I
needed to grow out of. Wasn't it enough that by the age of 10, I
had already begun the rite of passage into womanhood ushered
in by cramps and Kotex, complete with that lovely elastic belt to
hold them in place? Hadn't she noticed that my tender, budding
breasts were but a heartbeat away from that dreaded contraption
known as a "training" bra? Training for what?!

My body was growing into something completely foreign to
me; I felt as if I could no longer control it. Every night before
going to bed, I would observe this new body in my full-length
mirror, the changes seemingly occurring right before my eyes. I
began to touch this new body of mine, stimulating and teasing it,
loving the feeling of control that I did have over the way this
new body responded. I experimented and learned that, if I placed
my fingers between my legs just so and rubbed, that my new
body would respond by giving me a feeling of immense pleasure
unlike no other thing on earth had yet to give. I became creative,
using pillows and stuffed animals to hump my way to euphoria.

I wondered if this was a part of the "growing out" process that
Momma had spoke of and I really wanted to ask her about it, but
then decided it was probably best to keep this discovery to
myself.

There were many weird and wonderful things that happened

during my 10th year; the neighborhood boys started having strange reactions to my new body. No longer was I the first one picked for back-alley hardball. Nope, the boys had other plans for me. I thought that I would never understand the intrigue associated with breasts and the all-consuming desire that compelled the boys to chase me down with hopes of copping a feel, until I met Pam.

Pam was 13 years old and my first girlfriend. She was a big girl from a big family, three girls and seven boys, all nestled together in a big house on the South Side of Chicago. She was tall and muscular, with skin the color of copper lying in the sunshine. Her hair was coal black and thick with curls that her mother kept neatly plaited in two large braids. Her family owned the house that my family rented; actually, we shared the house. Pam and her family lived downstairs, while me, Momma and Daddy occupied the upper level. I found this to be a pretty good set-up, convenient with built-in playmates. Pam's mom was all too happy to have me, an only child, down for dinner or to watch TV with the other kids. She thought it was so sad that my parents had deprived me of siblings.

Television was a staple of family life in the late '60s, and Pam's family had two. There was a huge console model in the living room which was reserved for company and adult viewing, as well as a smaller black-and-white that had been relegated to the kids to watch cartoons, *Batman* and — me and Pam's personal favorite — *The Girl From U.N.C.L.E.*

The black-and-white was located in the basement, which Pam's dad had converted into a living space, complete with two bedrooms and a full bath for three of Pam's brothers. When Pam and I wanted to watch our show, the boys would graciously leave and let us have the entire space to ourselves. They insisted that they could not be caught sitting around with our silly behinds watching no stupid girly show. That was fine with us; we would be able to watch April Dancer, *The Girl From U.N.C.L.E.*, in total peace, free from their terrorist antics.

April was brave and brilliant, always foiling the evil genius' best-laid plans to destroy the world. She was beautiful and graceful as she fought her way from the clutches of doom every week. Retrospectively, April Dancer was my first unattainable, obsessive crush. Pam and I would sit and watch her adventures religiously and after the show, re-enact the episode with precise accuracy and attention to detail. We'd cover it all, everything from the capture to the escape, which seemed to be the formula that every show was based upon. The only detail that we would somehow manage to overlook was THE KISS, and you know there would always be THE KISS.

Until one hot summer afternoon. There we were in the bedroom, eyes glued to the screen watching Miss April do her thing. The show ended and Pam and I began our post-show ritual. Pam, as usual, played April and I played the evil genius who held her captive. She had the secret formula and refused to give it to me. I threatened her; she was undaunted. I tried to tie her up; she struggled. I wrestled her to the floor, held her arms at her side and this time in a moment of abandon, I kissed her.

She kissed me back.

In our realm of adolescent reality, it was a serious kiss, you know the kind with tightly closed lips and eyes the way they did it on TV back in the '60s, when husbands and wives slept in separate beds and dykes were known as career women. Anyway, the kiss, tightly closed lips and all, sent a signal to my brain that transmitted a tremor to my belly which ultimately resulted in a warm moisture between my legs that registered as girl to girl lust and seeped its way into my preteen, regulation-white cotton underpants.

I couldn't breathe.

I knew I couldn't breathe, because if I took a breath, the world would end and I didn't want to be responsible for that.

Pam, on the other hand, was breathing — loud.

I could feel the warmth of her breath against my face and I could tell her body must have been reacting to the exact same signal because she tried to make herself rigid, but her body betrayed her and her legs fell open, just slightly, just enough to let me know something was going on. We continued to lie on the floor for quite some time, her breathing and me not breathing, because I don't think we knew what to do next. Then we both moved, simultaneously getting up, saying nothing, and going home.

When we saw each other the next day, we acted as if nothing

unusual had happened the day before. Although I concealed it in the presence of Pam, I was aching inside, wanting to be with her. I wondered if she felt the same way about me, I wondered if she too had rubbed herself every night since our kiss and if she did, I wondered when the wet came if she called out my name.

The day finally arrived.

I couldn't concentrate in school, I had no appetite, no desire to play "It" at recess time. I kept looking at the clock, urging time to hurry up and pass. And then it was time for the show. I remember feeling the way you do when you told somebody not to throw you a surprise party, but you didn't mean it and you hope they knew you didn't mean it and surprise you anyway. I sat on the edge of the bed, watching the show but no longer abie to see April, only Pam.

Pam was extremely quiet: She stared straight ahead, never taking her eyes off the screen, sitting perfectly still and erect. The air was thick with something, something akin to a charge of electricity that was growing stronger as the show approached its conclusion.

I was starting to fidget and sigh. I felt like the growing thing was suffocating me. As the credits began to roll, Pam became animated. She turned and stared at me, and then the growing thing began to push us together. I touched Pam's breasts through her thin, summer shirt; she quivered and placed her warm hand over mine.

We stood up and walked to the back bedroom. It was dark and neither of us could see; we just let the growing thing lead us. Pam slid down on her brother's bed, never letting go of my hand, pulling me down on top of her. We lay together in the darkness, not speaking but somehow knowing that what was happening between us would always have to be hidden and secret. Our bodies began to push into each other and I started to kiss Pam in the only way that I knew how.

I was not prepared for her to slip her tongue into my mouth.

I felt the wet and opened my thighs wide, rubbing frantically against her; she was breathing hard, emitting little whimpers into my mouth as our tongues probed and explored. We came that way, rolling on top of each other humping and moaning the sound of our yet-to-be-named passion into each other's throats.

In this dark place, we lay panting, holding each other tight, the growing thing exploding and then subsiding into light.

Over the next three months, we replayed this scene many times, each joining more urgent and intense than the last. Soon, clothes were no longer a part of the equation. Naked and hot, we would ride each other. Fingers, searching slippery places, our flesh damp, made slapping sounds when we mashed together and sucking sounds when we pulled apart. We could no longer quiet our moans as we rode higher and higher, climbing over each other, into each other, until finally we would fall spent and satisfied into the safety of each other's arms.

We both forgot about April that summer.

I never wanted this thing between us to end, but as the seasons changed and school days were upon us, the chilly breeze of fall was not the only coldness that I felt. Pam, now 14, was heading in a different direction. She was entering high school, finding new interests and making new friends. I could only be with her from a distance now; she had placed a space between us that was impossible for me to bridge. Our world together had closed in on itself and soon dissipated with the falling leaves. My dad's company temporarily transferred us to St. Louis later that year. Pam said good-bye to me, with what seemed to be a sigh of relief. I said good-bye to her and felt heartbreak for the first time.

I often thought of Pam over the years, each memory a bittersweet mixture of both love and pain. There were other loves after her as I grew into my lesbian-woman self, but she always remained my most precious one.

Years later, back home in Chicago, I ran into Pam again. She was walking through the financial district downtown and I recognized her from half a block away. It was the end of summer and her skin glowed a burnished bronze. She was even taller now, and her braids had been replaced by a cascade of black waves that rested on her shoulders. As a woman, she had evolved into a goddess-like vision of black Amazon beauty, head held high as she worked her red sling-back pumps up LaSalle Street.

We caught up to each other and Pam shot a passing glance in my direction, never breaking her furious rush-hour pace. I still wonder to this day, if she hadn't stopped, would I have stopped her. But she did stop. She turned abruptly to find me staring at her and gave me that "I know, I know you from somewhere but I can't remember where" look. I said her name and her face opened into a tooth-baring grin, as she stretched her arms wide to embrace me. We held each other close, a floodgate of emotions rushing over my body, and then broke away to do the customary stuff.

"Girl, it's been a long time! How's your Momma? How's your Daddy? Where are you working? Chile, you look GOOD!" Somehow we managed to find out that both our moms were fine, Pam's daddy had passed on, and my daddy had left home, but not before finally giving me a brother and a sister. I was at the university and she was working for the Board of Trade.

Then Pam told me that she was married to a cop with two kids of her own. I must admit that I was somewhat disappointed to hear that because from the moment I saw her, I had thought of what it would be like to roll around together now, both of us grown and knowing what we liked. I let the moment pass and told her that I wasn't married but did have a girlfriend and assured her that I would never have kids.

She threw her head back and let out a deep, throaty laugh that sent cold fire to my very soul. She was still laughing, body shaking, barely able to get out her next question — "You mean you never grew out of that?"

I looked at her, old open wounds finally closing. I answered her question by embracing her again, I knew for the last time. Slowly, my head shook a no into the softness of her neck, then I whispered into her ear, "I guess I never will."

I Lost It at the Movies
by Jewelle Gomez

My grandmother, Lydia, and my mother, Dolores, were both
talking to me from their bathroom stalls in the Times Square
movie theatre. I was washing the popcorn butter from my hands
at the sink and didn't think it at all odd. The people in my family
are always talking; conversation is a life force in our world. My
great-grandmother, Grace, would narrate her life story from 7:00
A.M. until we went to bed at night. The only breaks were when
we were reading, or the reverential periods when we sat looking
out of our tenement windows observing the neighborhood —
whose sights we naturally talked about later.

So it was not odd that Lydia and Dolores were talking nonstop
from their stalls, oblivious to everyone except the three of us. I
hadn't expected it to happen there. I hadn't really expected an "it"
to happen at all. To be a lesbian is part of who I am, like being
left-handed. It seemed a fact that needed no articulation. My first
encounter with the word *bulldagger* was not charged with
emotional conflict. When I was a teenager in the 1960s, my
grandmother told me a story about a particular building in our
Boston neighborhood that had gone to seed. She described the
building's glorious past through the experience of a party she'd
attended there twenty years before. The best part of the evening
had been a woman she'd met and danced with.

Lydia had been a professional dancer and singer on the Black
theatre circuit: to dance with women was part of who she was.
They danced at the party, then the woman walked her home and
asked her out. I heard the delicacy of my grandmother's search
for the right words, even in the retelling. She'd explained to the
bulldagger, as she called her, that she liked her fine but was more
interested in men. As she spoke I was struck with how careful
my grandmother had been to make it clear to that woman (and,
in effect, to me) that there was no offense taken in her attentions,
that she just didn't "go that way." I was so happy at thirteen to
have a word for what I knew myself to be. The word was myste-
rious and curious, as if from a new language that used some
other alphabet. It left nothing familiar to cling to when touching

123

curves and crevices. Now a word existed, though, and my grandmother was not flinching in using it. In fact, she'd smiled at the good heart and dashing good looks of the bulldagger who'd liked her.

Once I had the knowledge of the word and a sense of its importance to me, I didn't feel the need to explain, confess, or define my identity as a lesbian. The process of reclaiming my ethnic identity in this country was already all-consuming. Of course, in different situations later on — some political, some not — I did make declarations. But not usually because I had to. Mostly they were declarations made to test the waters. A preparation for the rest of the world which, unlike my grandmother, might not have a grounding in what true love is about.

My first lover, the woman who'd been in my bed once a week through most of our high school years, married when we were twenty. After my writing started being published, I told her with my poems that I was a lesbian. She was not afraid to ask if what she'd read was about her and my love for her. So there, amidst her growing children and bowling trophies, I said yes, the poems were about my love for her. She did not pull back. And when I go home to visit my family I visit her. We sit across the kitchen table from each other, describing our lives and making jokes in the same way that we have for over twenty-five years.

During the 1970s I focused less on having a career than on how to eat and be creative simultaneously. Graduate school and a string of nontraditional jobs (stage manager, mid-town messenger, etc.) kept me so busy I had no time to think about my identity and its many layers. It was several years before I made the connection between my desire, my social isolation, and the difficulty I had with my writing. I thought of myself as a lesbian-between-girlfriends. Except the between had lasted five years.

After some anxiety and frustration I deliberately set about meeting women. Actually, I already knew many women. Including my closest friend back then, another Black woman who also worked in theatre. I tried opening up to her and explained my frustration at going to the parties we attended. I'd dance with men and keep up a good stream of patter, but inside my mind was racing, speculating on who might be someone I'd really be interested in. All the while I was too afraid to approach any women I was attracted to, certain I would be rejected because the women were either straight and horrified, or lesbian and terrified of being exposed. My friend listened with a pleasant, distant smile. Theoretical homosexuality was acceptable, and male homosexuality was even trendy. But my expression of the complexity and sometimes pain of the situation made her uncharacteristically obtuse. She became impatient and unsympathetic. I drifted away from her in pursuit of the women's community, a phrase that was not in my vocabulary yet, but I knew it was something more than just women. I fell into that community by connecting with other women writers, which helped me to focus on my writing as well as on my social life as a lesbian.

Yet none of these experiences demanded that I bare my soul. I remained honest but not explicit. *Expediency, diplomacy, discretion* are the words that come to mind now. At that time I knew no political framework through which to filter my lesbian experience. I was more preoccupied with the Attica riots than with Stonewall. Since the media helps to focus the public's attention within a proscribed spectrum, obscuring the connections between issues, I worried about who would shelter Angela Davis. The concept of sexual politics was remote and theoretical.

I'm not certain exactly when and where a theory converged with my reality. Being a Black woman and a lesbian blended unexpectedly for me like that famous scene in Ingmar Bergman's film *Persona*. The different faces came together as one, and my desire became part of my heritage, my skin, my perspective, my politics, and my future. I was certain that it had been my past that helped make the future possible. The women in my family had acted as if their lives were meaningful. Their lives were art. To be a lesbian among them was to be an artist. Perhaps the convergence came when I saw the faces of my great-grandmother, grandmother, and mother in those of the community of women I finally connected with. There was the same adventurous glint in their eyes, the same determined step, the penchant for breaking into song and for not waiting for anyone to take care of them.

I needed not to pretend to be other than who I was with any of these women in my family. Did I need to declare it? During the holidays when I brought home best friends/lovers, my family welcomed us warmly, clasping us to their magnificent bosoms. Yet there was always an element of silence in our neighborhood and in our home. It was disturbing to me, pressing against me more persistently each year. During visits to Boston, it no longer sufficed that Lydia and Dolores were loving and kind to the "friend" I had with me. Maybe it was just my getting older. Living in New York City at the age of thirty-two in 1980, there was little I kept deliberately hidden from anyone. Although the genteel silence that hovered around me when I entered my mother's or grandmother's apartments was palpable, I was unsure whether it was already there when I arrived or if I carried it home within myself. It cut me off from what I knew was a kind of fulfillment available only from my family. The lifeline from Grace to Lydia to Dolores to Jewelle is a strong one. We are bound by so many things, not the least of which is looking so much alike. I was not willing to be orphaned by silence.

If the idea of church weddings and station wagons holds no appeal for me, the concept of an extended family is certainly important. But my efforts were stunted by my family's inability to talk about the life I was creating for myself, for all of us. The silence felt all the more foolish because I thought I knew how my family would react. I was confident they would respond with their customary aplomb, just as they had when I'd first had my hair cut into an Afro (which they hated), or when I brought home friends who were vegetarians (which they found curious). While we had disagreed about issues, like the fight my mother and I had over Viet Nam when I was nineteen, always when the deal went down we sided with each other. Somewhere deep inside I think I believed that neither my grandmother nor my mother would ever censure my choices. Neither had actually raised me; my great-grandmother had done that. Grace had been a steely barricade against any encroachment on our personal freedoms, and she'd rarely disapproved out loud of any considered decision I'd made.

But it was not enough to have an unabashed admiration for these women. To have pride in how they'd so graciously survived in spite of the odds against them was easy. It was something else to be standing in a Times Square movie theatre faced with the chance to say "it" out loud and risk the loss of their brilliant and

126

benevolent smiles.

My mother had started reading the graffiti written on the wall of the bathroom cubicle. We hooted at each of her dramatic renderings. Then she said (not breaking rhythm, since we all know timing is everything), "Here's one I haven't seen before — DYKES UNITE." There was that profound silence again, as if the frames of my life had ground to a halt in a projector. We were in a freeze-frame, and options played themselves out in my head in rapid succession: Say nothing? Say something? Say what?

I laughed and said, "Yeah, but have you seen the rubber stamp on my desk at home?"

"No," said my mother, with a slight bit of puzzlement. "What's it say?"

"I saw it," my grandmother called out from her stall. "It says Lesbian Money."

"What?"

"LESBIAN MONEY," Lydia repeated loudly over the water running in the row of sinks.

"I just stamp it on my big bills," I said tentatively, and we all screamed with laughter. The other women in the restroom had only been a shadow for me in these moments, but they came into focus as I felt each one press more closely to her sink, trying to pretend that the conversation was not happening.

Since that night there has been little said on the subject. Yet. There have been some awkward moments, usually in social situations where Lydia or Dolores felt uncertain.

A couple of years after our Times Square encounter I visited my grandmother for the weekend with my lover. One of the neighbors in her building dropped by, and when she left, my grandmother spoke to me in low tones while my lover was in another room. She said we should be careful about being so open in front of other people because they weren't necessarily as fair-minded as she. I was flooded, momentarily, with shock and disappointment. But before I could respond, she heard the words and their incongruity with who she was. She grabbed my arm and demanded, "Forget I said that. Nobody pays rent around this apartment but me."

We have not explored "it," but the shift in our relationship is clear. I feel free to be an adult, and my family has the chance to

127

see me as such.

I'm lucky. My family was as relieved as I was to finally know who I am.

Interview with Stephanie Byrd
by Terri Jewell

[Stephanie Byrd is a Black lesbian feminist poet, writer, critic, community activist. Her works include two books of poetry; critical essays in Greenwood Press' *Bibliography of Contemporary Lesbian Literature* (1993) and *Lesbian Review of Books* (1995); listing in *Black Lesbians: An Annotated Bibliography* by J.R. Roberts (1981); mention in Ann Allen Shockley's essay, "The Black Lesbian in American Literature: An Overview" (1979) and *Black Women and the Sexual Mountain* by Calvin Hernton (1988). Her poetry has appeared in *The American Voice, Kenyon Review, Conditions* and *Sinister Wisdom*. Her books have been reviewed by many publications.]

STEPHANIE BYRD: I was born in 1950 on July 10th in Richmond, Indiana. My family has lived in or around Richmond since the War of 1812, perhaps before then. Part of them came from Boston, Massachusetts because the Northwest Territory was free territory and they did not wish to become enslaved again. Other members of my family escaped from slavery in the South and came to Indiana, where small Black settlements had sprung up. These are the people that I came from.

I was a Latin major at Ball State University from 1968-1969 and was an anti-war activist from 1968-1973. I met some civil rights activists during that period who were doing work in Cairo, Illinois. The Black community in Cairo was boycotting the white businesses because of their refusal to hire Blacks. The white community was responding by driving through the Black community at night and shooting through people's windows, so after dark people would turn out the lights and sit on the floor. I met a man who was doing some fund-raising at Indiana University in Bloomington and became involved with gathering canned goods and clothing to offset "The Wolf" in Cairo until the problem could be resolved.

TERRI JEWELL: Were you a lesbian then?

BYRD: Yes. When I was about 6 or 7, one of the neighbors called me a lesbian. I went to my grandmother and asked her about it and she told me that being a lesbian was about loving women, women loving women.

JEWELL: Your grandmother told you that?!!

BYRD: Yes. My grandmother Byrd. And that it was all right to be a lesbian if I really loved someone. And since I was in love with my little next door neighbor, I went out and told everyone that we were lesbians. My mother was furious and I think that was the first time I heard about lesbians. The second time, I was 12 and I was asked to put down on a sheet of paper what my goals in life were. I was in the seventh grade at Hibbard Elementary/Junior High School. I had put down that my goals were to be a brain surgeon, a lawyer, and a lesbian. I was sent to the office. I realized when I was sent down to the office that something was terribly wrong even though I was only 12, and they said, "Well, do you know what a lesbian is?" And I said, "It's a person who lives on the isle of Lesbos," because I had looked it up in the dictionary. They let me go, feeling secure that I really didn't know what I was talking about. It's funny that about a year later I was sent to the office again for being a Communist.

JEWELL: A Communist?

BYRD: Yes, because I asked for the Communist Manifesto in the school library so we could compare it to the Declaration of Independence.
When I was about 17, I realized that there was something wrong with being a lesbian socially. I tried to become straight and hooked up with this guy who turned out to be gay. By the time I was 19, I realized that none of this was working, so I just went back to being a lesbian again. It was very hard, though, because at 19 you're kind of a sexual libertine. You're not straight, you're not gay. You're just in heat. Being a lesbian was just the best and easiest way for me to be.

JEWELL: When did you start writing?

BYRD: When I was 17, in the summer. I had actually started writing before then during that school year and had written some short stories and some poetry. When I graduated from high school, I started writing poetry seriously and actually had a ˙ contest with my little gay boyfriend. We would write a book of poetry a month and that summer I produced three books of poetry, all of which I burned.

JEWELL: Why?

BYRD: I have destroyed my work in the past. I'd say, all together, four books of poetry. I have a tendency to lose control of my temper and as a result, my reason. I would burn my work as a cleansing act. A ritual.

JEWELL: You don't consider the act of writing a cleansing? A ritual?

BYRD: Writing can be cleansing, but there have been times in my life when even the writing is not enough to cleanse.

JEWELL: So, writing is not always enough to cleanse what?

BYRD: Oh, I call them "the Terrors." They are anxieties and fears that somehow combine into a feeling so large they seem to consume me from the inside out. I think some actress in a Neil Simon play once called them the "Red Meanies."

JEWELL: What has survived of your writing?

BYRD: There is a book of poetry called *25 Years of Malcontent* which is now out of print. When I finished *25 Years of Malcontent*, it was the result of serious years of serious writing, the last three of which I wrote every day for at least two hours a day, sometimes eight, depending on whether or not I was employed. It was released in 1976 and published by Good Gay Poets in Boston. As with most first works by a writer, it's somewhat autobiographical, describing things and events that I observed or was involved in. There is one poem there about a

131

man who died in a house. He wasn't found until much later and his cats had tried to chew through the door to get to him to eat him because they hadn't been fed. And there is a poem about a white suffragette I had met in Texas. She was a wonderful, wonderful woman well into her 60s. This was in 1972. She told me to be true to my roots. The advice that she gave me was very good advice. The whole time I was in Boston, I don't think I ever really convinced myself that I was anything but a Black woman from Indiana.

JEWELL: When did you first go to Boston?

BYRD: It was 1973.

JEWELL: Were you aware of the Combahee River Collective then?

BYRD: In 1974, the women who eventually evolved into the Combahee River Collective* were the National Black Feminist Organization of which I was a member. We used to meet as a support group at the Women's Center in Cambridge. We would talk about a number of things. Barbara Smith was there and she developed guidelines on how we were to support each other. It was very much like consciousness-raising. I remember the group being an open group and a lot of women coming who were straight and battered. They were Black women. Some of them were successful, some of them were very poor, some of them were working-class women. There were incidents where outsid-

---

* Combahee River Collective — a Black feminist group in Boston whose name comes from the guerrilla action conceptualized and led by Harriet Tubman on June 2, 1863, in the Port Royal region of South Carolina. This action freed more than 750 slaves and is the only military campaign in American history planned and led by a woman. [from *This Bridge Called My Back: Writings by Radical Women of Color*, edited by Cherríe Moraga and Gloria Anzaldúa; published by Kitchen Table Women of Color Press.]

ers would come and discover that there were Black lesbians there and they would flip out with a great deal of hysteria and arguing and name-calling. And those were the early meetings. But the thing I remember is these women coming who had been so battered in their lives that there was something disturbing about them and a support group wasn't going to do it for them. I heard someone say recently that one of the best cures for mental illness for Black people is Black culture and I wanted the group to be more committed to the creation and preservation of Black women's culture. But that was really difficult to do with the Combahee River Collective because the group soon was not all Black. And the support group was very much committed to combating racism and sexism and anti-Semitism and class oppression, so many minority women had to be included. At that time, I had a great deal of difficulty synthesizing the presence and the issues of the minority women who were not Black into the issues that involved me. I was something of a Black separatist, I suppose.

JEWELL: In reading their statement, the group was against separatism and wanted to work with Black men.

BYRD: Well, I never heard them say anything about working with any men when I was in the group. They talked about working with white women. [In attempting to address] all the other concerns [of Koreans, Hispanics, Jews, Chinese, Vietnamese, etc.] just turned into a wave that seemed to obliterate what I was hoping would become a Black feminist support group. And as Black feminists, in retrospect, I realize now that I was hoping that we could do something to address the needs of some of these women who were coming to us who had been stabbed or shot or beaten and threatened and didn't know how to leave their husbands or didn't know how to address life without a man. These women needed a separatist environment in which to heal. Maybe later on, this whole multi-ethnic feminist vanguard could include them, but for then and for now, too, it doesn't. It does not address the needs of these Black women.

JEWELL: I agree. So, why do you think that is, even though we are well-versed in the problems that we have? And I'm not living on either the East or the West coasts, but in the Midwest. You know the gaps HERE. In your opinion, why are we Black women so afraid of having our own groups and projects exclusively? We always talk about how nice it is to be among ourselves with our own language and our own ways of doing and seeing things, but we just don't do it. Even the Combahee River Statement says, "We realize that the only people who care enough about us to work consistently for our liberation are us." Yet, we are constantly getting away from that.

BYRD: Oh, it's much easier to address everyone else's needs rather than your own. You know that from dealing with your own problems. It is much easier to go out and find someone else who has a bigger problem or a different problem and work on their problem for them than to deal with your own mess. And essentially, that's what we have been doing all along historically. We think we CAN'T do it by ourselves. And the reason why we can't do it by ourselves is because "they" will annihilate us. We have to get away from this paranoia.

JEWELL: How long were you with this group?

BYRD: Oh, until about 1976.

JEWELL: So, it did not start out being a Black *lesbian* group?

BYRD: Oh, no, no, no.

JEWELL: Or did it start out being a Black lesbian group but no one was saying this just so more women would want to be involved without stigma?

BYRD: When the group started, there were only three of us, including myself, who said they were lesbians. Only three of us announced that we were lesbians during the first night of the group. The other women introduced themselves by talking about where they went to graduate school and what their interests were, etc., but no one else said they were lesbians. After several months, though, some of the other women came out.

134

JEWELL: What made you leave the group?

BYRD: I was heavily into my poetry, doing a lot of writing and readings. And I wanted to do more cultural things. I read all over Boston: University of Massachusetts, Boston; Fanuiel Hall, which is the Town Hall in Boston. In 1976 I decided I couldn't maintain the separatist pose any longer, that I would have to become involved with the Gay and Lesbian Rights Movement.

JEWELL: Why couldn't you maintain a separatist stance?

BYRD: Actually, I found that despite what the Combahee River Collective said about separatism, they were very anti-male. Most of the women I knew there did not like men and made no pretense of acting like they liked men or wanted to do anything to help men. I had met a lot of Black gay men who had been decent to me and had been brotherly. I felt the least I could do was return in kind. So I became more involved in the Gay and Lesbian Rights Movement but always, ALWAYS my focus was on US as a Black people. Not just as Black women but as Black people. And in writing my poetry, because I am a Black woman, I was creating Black women's culture. And those things were becoming clearer and clearer to me as I grew older. And I didn't need a large support group to give me an identity. My identity was growing out of MY growing as a Black woman artist and creating Black women's art. And as a Black person who has a Black father and Black male cousins and Black uncles and a Black grandfather, I had a duty to protect their rights as Black people. The only way I could do that, because I couldn't do it within the homophobic Black community, was to do it with the Gay and Lesbian Rights Movement.

JEWELL: You were on television and the radio?

BYRD: In 1977, I was a guest on a Black cultural TV program called *Mzizi Roots*. This was an Emmy award-winning program in Boston. I appeared on the segment called "Gay Rights — Whose Rights?" and the host was Sarah Ann Shaw. The other two guests were a Black psychologist and a Black gay male activist. We discussed the presence of Black lesbians and gays in the Black community and the legitimacy of claims made by gay and lesbian activist groups for human rights. I also did radio programs. I did one called *Coming Out* and that was in 1974. I was asked a whole bunch of questions about Black lesbianism. This was on PBS [Public Broadcasting Service]. Then I did another radio program, *Out of the Closet*, in 1978. By then, I was reading poetry on the air. I had a small group starting with two women and ending up as a five-piece band, called Hermanas. They used to accompany my poetry with music. They were with me until 1982. Then, in 1984 I did a whole one-hour show on MIT [Massachusetts Institute of Technology] radio called *Musically Speaking*, which was nothing but poetry and music. I also read for Rock Against Sexism, which was the name of a group of punk rockers in 1984. That was at the Massachusetts College of Art. I read in New York for the Open Line Poetry Series at Washington Square Church in 1983; in Newburyport, MA; all over Cambridge. I was very, very active.

JEWELL: Tell me about your second book.

BYRD: My second book is self-published, *A Distant Footstep On The Plain*. It was the late 1970's. I had been asked to read some poetry at International Women's Day at Cambridge's YWCA. I read a poem called "On Black Women Dying." It deals with Black women I have known who have died and the Black women who were murdered in Boston whose murders were never solved. It was a kind of a serial killing. I read this poem with the accompaniment of music. That's where Hermanas made its first appearance. It was a conga and a guitar. After that, I got telephone calls to do it again, so we got together and we performed more.

> ... in the fall of 1978
> the Klan began
> its "open recruitment"
> in the Boston City schools
> and it was 1955

136

that a team of white professionals
interviewed colored children
from the Wayne County school system
as to whether their mammas and daddies
was for integration
or segregation
well, what i'm trying to get at
is that in the last 30 odd years
of my life span
there has occurred
a series of events
which have culminated
in the death and near dying
of Black women
across the continent of Amerika ...

In 1979 I became unemployed, so I had more time to write. I was moving furniture and doing odd jobs around the city. It was a tough period in my life. I was hungry a lot.

JEWELL: So, how did you self-publish your second book, *A Distant Footstep On The Plain*?

BYRD: I was working on the Boston and Maine Railroad at the time I finished my second book and I couldn't find a publisher for it. I self-published my book in 1983. I went to printers and did a cost comparison. I had a friend who was a typographer and she worked on my manuscript. She gave me the negative for my book so that I could get it published. She did this work for free. We took it to a local, small neighborhood newspaper that donated their space and we laid out the book in 24 hours. And then we drove it to the printer's, it went to press, and a week later I went back and picked up three crates of it. It cost me $600 for 600 copies.

JEWELL: Why the title *A Distant Footstep On The Plain*?

BYRD: I am from Indiana. In a sense, it is my being true to my roots. It is a reaffirmation of who I am and where I'm from. A distant footstep on the plain. That's what I was at one time.

I have a manuscript in the works now. It's tentatively entitled *In The House of Coppers*. I feel good about this work. It feels better than the second book. It's a different kind of work, probably closer to the first work. Maybe it's a new threshold for me.

JEWELL: Which writers do you enjoy?

BYRD: Bessie Head, a South African, and her works *Serowe: Village of the Rainwind* and *Collector of Treasures*. I'm very fond of Samuel Delaney, the Black science fiction writer, and Octavia Butler, another Black science fiction writer. I dream of Toni Morrison and I like Gloria Naylor a lot. They are superior writers. There are a lot of African writers that I like: Ferdinand Oyono, who wrote *The Old Man And The Medal*; Yambo Ouloguem, who wrote *Bound To Violence*; Mariama Ba, who was a very fine writer. I also enjoy Simone Schwarz-Bart, a Caribbean writer who wrote *The Bridge of Beyond* and the poetry of Marilyn Hacker and William Carlos Williams and Nicolas Guillén. I also have to give a nod to Sexton and Plath, though their work doesn't interest me as much as it did when I was in my 20s.

It Happened One Sunday Afternoon
by L.K. Barnett

Most 15-year-old girls experience a major crush on one of
two types of adolescent males. There is the scrawny, lanky guy
who really isn't cute or outgoing, but he's sweet and knows how
to make the awkward and vulnerable pubescent female feel
special. Then there is the "macho" jock, who is cute and even
has a little hair on his face to prove the presence of testosterone.

I was different. I met Vita, which isn't her real name, when I
was 15. We met at church. I was sitting on the pew beside my
grandmother when Vita, who was several pews before us, turned
around to see who was in the congregation. Our eyes met and no
one before then or since has ever given me a smile that said so
much.

That evening over supper I casually asked my grandmother
who that woman was. I described her as best as I could. That
wasn't very difficult, since I'd memorized her face in a matter of
seconds.

It didn't take my grandmother any time to name *that* woman.
She went on to tell me about Vita Rose. (I chose that pseudonym
because Vita means life, and roses were my love's favorite
flowers. Every time I see a rose I am reminded of her life and
how much she shaped mine.) Vita had been an elementary school
teacher and registered nurse. She'd been married to a photographer who had been well-known in the community. They'd had
two beautiful children, etc. Grandmother told me that day had
been the first Sunday Vita had been to church in quite some time.
She'd lost her husband and had been grieving for months.

The next Sunday, immediately following the benediction, I
approached Mrs. Rose. I was a little nervous, but I wanted this
woman to know me. The moments before I introduced myself
still seem suspended in time. I told her who I was, I mentioned
who my grandmother was (since I'd learned the previous Sunday
they had belonged to the same Women's Bible Class for over
thirty years). She was very cordial and told me to look her up in
the phone book and give her a call.

That evening I wrote Mrs. Rose a long letter filling her in on

139

the previous 15 years of my life. I wrote the whole evening long and mailed it the following morning. A couple of days passed; one evening, my grandmother's telephone rang. I knew the instant it rang it was Mrs. Rose. My grandmother called me to the phone, quite elated that such a nice woman — "educated, too" — had taken an interest in me. On the telephone, Mrs. Rose complimented my letter-writing style and told me she was very "impressed" with me. I explained to her that I was only visiting my grandmother and would be returning to my home state of Illinois at the end of the summer. We made plans to keep in touch.

Over the next two years I wrote hundreds of letters, and we both made AT&T richer! Vita was understanding, easy to talk to and always cheerful. She was constantly encouraging me and insisting I build big dreams. Her optimism was contagious. Vita listened well; she knew how to offer her advice without sounding harshly critical of my plans or ideas.

I found myself sharing every aspect of my life with Vita and looking forward to visits with my grandmother more than ever. I look back on those years now and realize that was the onset of my first lesbian relationship. The essence of a lesbian relationship is the spiritual and emotional connecting of two females — which can be celebrated through lovemaking and continuous nurturing of one another. I connected with Vita — despite the 50 years age difference.

During this time, I was messing around with high school boys because it was the "normal" thing to do. But in the back of my mind, thoughts of holding and kissing Vita were causing me to question my sexuality.

That was the spring my mother decided we'd surprise my grandmother for the "Mother's Day" holiday. I decided I would share my feelings with Vita. Of course, I was deathly fearful, yet there was no way around it. She had to know that thoughts of loving her had been occupying my mind.

That Sunday afternoon after church, I went home with Mrs. Rose. I will never forget the anxiety I felt. A small part of me feared rejection. In fact, it crossed my mind that I could lose the friendship I'd grown to cherish above all else. A greater part of me, however, sensed Vita harbored some of the same emotions.

140

I pray that the following memory never escapes me, and so by writing this I know our love is somewhat immortalized.

After we were inside of her house, Mrs. Rose asked me to unzip the back of her dress — she wanted to change into a housecoat. I held my breath while unzipping her dress. As I gently tugged on the zipper, which as luck would have it was difficult to manipulate, her bare skin became visible. I became fraught with an obscure mixture of desire, fear and anxiety.

She hung up her dress and sashayed around the room while I sat on the edge of the bed utterly stunned at how preserved — beautifully preserved — her body was. When Vita asked me why I was so quiet, I told her I had something very important to say. She sat down on the bed beside me, took my hand in her own and began to gently rub my back with her free hand. In this position, she lovingly coaxed the words out of me. In an almost inaudible voice, with my eyes cast on my lap, I whispered, "I'm in love with you and I want to make love with you." Vita was quiet for several seconds, which seemed like an eternity; then she casually said, "I feel the same way."

We spent the rest of the afternoon talking about the huge age difference, how people would react, how she could never "come out" and how we both arrived at the state we were in. We decided to be very careful so no one in her family or in her circle of friends would find out, and I falsely swore I would not share our affair with any of my friends.

I didn't exactly know how to make love to a woman, but on that afternoon nothing was more important to me than pleasing Vita. I wanted to know every inch of her and I wanted to know how it felt to experience lovemaking with someone who you know loves you. I hadn't considered what Vita could do for me; my thoughts were completely filled with how I could rejuvenate a love-starved soul.

Overwhelmed by the fact that she was crossing the line of physical intimacy — with a woman — Vita was actually too nervous to let any lovemaking take place. At least, she was on that particular Sunday afternoon. We spent the remainder of the evening holding each other. This picture remains clear in my memory: Vita in her white lace slip and thigh-high panty hose and me, still in my church dress. Before I left, Vita gave me a kiss — a long exploratory kiss — a promise kiss — a kiss that said "there will be more, just be patient." A kiss unlike any I'd ever experienced with a male.

That was the Sunday afternoon I came out to myself. It felt exhilarating. I knew in time I would have to share it with friends, and I did. Of course, I got the expected "She's too old" and "You need counseling." It didn't bother me, though, because for the first time I felt loved, and if I was a freak or she was a freak... then in my opinion, we were just two freaks in love. But how lucky I was to experience something so wonderful with someone so wonderful.

Vita and I spent two years together. It is an indescribable feeling when two souls collide in the safety of knowing their lover is filled with only the utmost care and kindness. I experienced this type of collision with Vita. She has since passed away, and mere words cannot accurately account for the void I feel within my heart. I know our love was strong because I feel her love from the grave. I hear her whispers of encouragement in the night winds, and on really difficult days — if I close my eyes — I can feel her embrace and even smell her fragrance: *White Shoulders*.

I regret we weren't able to display our love in the presence of others. I regret we had to go to so many measures to keep her family and friends ignorant about what was really going on. When I look back, though, I think some of them must have had an idea; you can't really disguise true love. I do not and will not ever regret "us" or the fact that I discovered me, and I discovered love and it all happened on one Sunday afternoon.

For my precious ROSE, I miss you beyond words, beyond sighs, tears and heartfelt moans. I can not explain the emptiness that has invaded my soul since your unexpected departure. Life is not nearly as sweet without you in it. My love for you is still growing.

Johnnieruth
by Becky Birtha

Summertime. Nighttime. Talk about steam heat. This whole
city get like the bathroom when somebody in there taking a
shower with the door shut. Nights like that, can't nobody sleep.
Everybody be outside, sitting on they steps or else dragging half
they furniture out on the sidewalk — kitchen chairs, card tables
— even bringing TVs outside.

Womenfolks, mostly. All the grown women around my way
look just the same. They all big — stout. They got big bosoms
and big hips and fat legs, and they always wearing runover
house-shoes, and them shapeless, flowered numbers with the
buttons down the front. Cept on Sunday. Sunday morning they
all turn into glamour girls, in them big hats and long gloves, with
they skinny high heels and they skinny selves in them tight
girdles — wouldn't nobody ever know what they look like the
rest of the time.

When I was a little kid I didn't wanna grow up, cause I never
wanted to look like them ladies. I heard Miz Jenkins down the
street one time say she don't mind being fat cause that way her
husband don't get so jealous. She say it's more than one way to
keep a man. Me, I don't have me no intentions of keeping no
man. I never understood why they was in so much demand
anyway, when it seem like all a woman can depend on em for is
making sure she keep on having babies.

We got enough children in my neighborhood. In the summertime, even the little kids allowed to stay up till eleven or twelve
o'clock at night — playing in the street and hollering and carrying on — don't never seem to get tired. Don't nobody care, long
as they don't fight.

Me — I don't hang around no front steps no more. Hot nights
like that, I get out my ten speed and I be gone.

That's what I like to do more than anything else in the whole
world. Feel that wind in my face keeping me cool as a air
conditioner, shooting along like a snowball. My bike light as a
kite. I can really get up some speed.

All the guys around my way got ten speed bikes. Some of the

143

girls got em too, but they don't ride em at night. They pedal around during the day, but at nighttime they just hang around out front, watching babies and running they mouth. I didn't get my Peugeot to be no conversation piece.

My mama don't like me to ride at night. I tried to point out to her that she ain't never said nothing to my brothers, and Vincent a year younger than me. (And Langston two years older, in case "old" is the problem.) She say, "That's different, Johnnieruth. You're a girl." Now I wanna know how is anybody gonna know that. I'm skinny as a knifeblade turned sideways, and all I ever wear is blue jeans and a Wrangler jacket. But if I bring that up, she liable to get started in on how come I can't be more of a young lady, and fourteen is old enough to start taking more pride in my appearance, and she gonna be ashamed to admit I'm her daughter.

I just tell her that my bike be moving so fast can't nobody hardly see me, and couldn't catch me if they did. Mama complain to her friends how I'm wild and she can't do nothing with me. She know I'm gonna do what I want no matter what she say. But she know I ain't getting in no trouble, neither.

Like some of the boys I know stole they bikes, but I didn't do nothing like that. I'd been saving my money ever since I can remember, every time I could get a nickel or a dime outta anybody.

When I was a little kid, it was hard to get money. Seem like the only time they ever give you any was on Sunday morning, and then you had to put it in the offering. I used to hate to do that. In fact, I used to hate everything about Sunday morning. I had to wear all them ruffly dresses — that shiny slippery stuff in the wintertime that got to make a noise every time you move your ass a inch on them hard old benches. And that scratchy starchy stuff in the summertime with all them scratchy crinolines. Had to carry a pocketbook and wear them shiny shoes. And the church we went to was all the way over on Summit Avenue, so the whole damn neighborhood could get a good look. At least all the other kids'd be dressed the same way. The boys think they slick cause they get to wear pants, but they still got to wear a white shirt and a tie; and them dumb hats they wear can't hide them baldheaded haircuts, cause they got to take the hats off

144

in church.

There was one Sunday when I musta been around eight. I remember it was before my sister Corletta was born, cause right around then was when I put my foot down about that whole sanctimonious routine. Anyway, I was dragging my feet along Twenty-fifth Street in back of Mama and Vincent and them, when I spied this lady. I only seen her that one time, but I still remember just how she look. She don't look like nobody I ever seen before. I *know* she don't live around here. She real skinny. But she ain't no real young woman, neither. She could be old as my mama. She ain't nobody's mama — I'm sure. And she ain't wearing Sunday clothes. She got on blue jeans and a man's blue working shirt, with the tail hanging out. She got patches on her blue jeans, and she still got her chin stuck out like she some kinda African royalty. She ain't carrying no shiny pocketbook. It don't look like she care if she got any money or not, or who know it, if she don't. She ain't wearing no house-shoes, or stockings or high heels neither.

Mama always speak to everybody, but when she pass by this lady she make like she ain't even seen her. But I get me a real good look, and the lady stare right back at me. She got a funny look on her face, almost like she think she know me from some place. After she pass on by, I had to turn around to get another look, even though Mama say that ain't polite. And you know what? She was turning around, too, looking back at me. And she give me a great big smile.

I didn't know too much in them days, but that's when I first got to thinking about how it's got to be different ways to be, from the way people be around my way. It's got to be places where it don't matter to nobody if you all dressed up on Sunday morning or you ain't. That's how come I started saving money. So, when I got enough, I could go away to some place like that.

Afterwhile I begun to see there wasn't no point in waiting around for handouts, and I started thinking of ways to earn my own money. I used to be running errands all the time — mailing letters for old Grandma Whittaker and picking up cigarettes and newspapers up the corner for everybody. After I got bigger, I started washing cars in the summer, and shoveling people sidewalk in the wintertime. Now I got me a newspaper route.

Ain't never been no girl around here with no paper route, but I guess everybody got it figured out by now that I ain't gonna be like nobody else.

The reason I got me my Peugeot was so I could start to explore. I figured I better start looking around right now, so when I'm grown, I'll know exactly where I wanna go. So I ride around every chance I get.

Last summer, I used to ride with the boys a lot. Sometimes eight or ten of us'd just go cruising around the streets together. All of a sudden my mama decide she don't want me to do that no more. She say I'm too old to be spending so much time with boys. (That's what they tell you half the time, and the other half the time they worried cause you ain't interested in spending more time with boys. Don't make much sense.) She want me to have some girl friends, but I never seem to fit in with none of the things the girls doing. I used to think I fit in more with the boys.

But I seen how Mama might be right, for once. I didn't like the way the boys was starting to talk about girls sometimes. Talking about what some girl be like from the neck on down, and talking all up underneath somebody clothes and all. Even though I wasn't really friends with none of the girls, I still didn't like it. So now I mostly just ride around by myself. And Mama don't like that neither — you just can't please her.

This boy that live around the corner on North Street, Kenny Henderson, started asking me one time if I don't ever be lonely, cause he always see me by myself. He say don't I ever think I'd like to have me somebody special to go places with and stuff. Like I'd pick him if I did! Made me wanna laugh in his face. I do be lonely, a lotta times, but I don't tell nobody. And I ain't met nobody yet that I'd really rather be with than be by myself. But I will someday. When I find that special place where everybody different, I'm gonna find somebody there I can be friends with. And it ain't gonna be no dumb boy.

I found me one place already, that I like to go to a whole lot. It ain't even really that far away — by bike — but it's on the other side of the Avenue. So I don't tell Mama and then I go there, cause they like to think I'm right around the neighborhood someplace. But this neighborhood too dull for me. All the houses look just the same — no porches, no yards, no trees — not even

146

no parks around here. Every block look so much like every other block it hurt your eyes to look at, afterwhile. So I ride across Summit Avenue and go down that big steep hill there, and then make a sharp right at the bottom and cross the bridge over the train tracks. Then I head on out the boulevard — that's the nicest part, with all them big trees making a tunnel over the top, and lightning bugs shining in the bushes. At the end of the boulevard you get to this place call the Plaza.

It's something like a little park — the sidewalks is all bricks and they got flowers planted all over the place. The same kind my mama grow in that painted-up tire she got out front masquerading like a garden decoration — only seem like they smell sweeter here. It's a big high fountain right in the middle, and all the streetlights is the real old-fashion kind. That Plaza is about the prettiest place I ever been.

Sometimes something going on there. Like a orchestra playing music or some man or lady singing. One time they had a show with some girls doing some kinda foreign dances. They look like they were around my age. They all had on these fancy costumes, with different color ribbons all down they back. I wouldn't wear nothing like that, but it looked real pretty when they was dancing.

I got me a special bench in one corner where I like to sit, cause I can see just about everything, but wouldn't nobody know I was there. I like to sit still and think, and I like to watch people. A lotta people be coming there at night — to look at the shows and stuff, or just to hang out and cool off. All different kinda people.

This one night when I was sitting over in that corner where I always be at, there was this lady standing right near my bench. She mostly had her back turned to me and she didn't know I was there, but I could see her real good. She had on this shiny purple shirt and about a million silver bracelets. I kinda liked the way she look. Sorta exotic, like she maybe come from California or one of the islands. I mean she had class — standing there posing with her arms folded. She walk away a little bit. Then turn around and walk back again. Like she waiting for somebody.

Then I spotted this dude coming over. I spied him all the way cross the Plaza. Looking real fine. Got on a three piece suit. One

of them little caps sitting on a angle. Look like leather. He
coming straight over to this lady I'm watching and then she seen
him too and she start to smile, but she don't move till he get right
up next to her. And then I'm gonna look away, cause I can't stand
to watch nobody hugging and kissing on each other, but all of a
sudden I see it ain't no dude at all. It's another lady.

Now I can't stop looking. They smiling at each other like they
ain't seen one another in ten years. Then the one in the purple
shirt look around real quick — but she don't look just behind her
— and sorta pull the other one right back into the corner where
I'm sitting at, and then they put they arms around each other and
kiss — for a whole long time. Now I really know I oughtta turn
away, but I can't. And I know they gonna see me when they
finally open they eyes. And they do.

They both kinda gasp and back up, like I'm the monster that
just rose up outta the deep. And then I guess they can see I'm
only a girl, and they look at one another — and start to laugh!
Then they just turn around and start to walk away like it wasn't
nothing at all. But right before they gone, they both look around
again, and see I still ain't got my eye muscles and jaw muscles
working right again yet. And the one lady wink at me. And the
other one say, "Catch you later."

I can't stop staring at they backs, all the way across the Plaza.
And then, all of a sudden, I feel like I got to be doing something,
got to be moving.

I wheel on outta the Plaza and I'm just concentrating on
getting up my speed. Cause I can't figure out what to think.
Them two women kissing and then, when they get caught, just
laughing about it. And here I'm laughing too, for no reason at all.
I'm sailing down the boulevard laughing like a lunatic, and then
I'm singing at the top of my lungs. And climbing that big old hill
up to Summit Avenue is just as easy as being on a escalator.

Lavender Sheep in the Fold
by Donna Allegra

The upshot of my lesbian identity is that I fall in love with female people — and want to. I don't see this as a "lifestyle" — such a temporary-sounding term. It brings to mind this season's fall fashions or a layout of home decoration in the manner of the Tudor kings. My lesbianism is more the ground zero of an emotional compass, ever searching out women. This orientation of my heart is not going to change because I don't want it to.

I've never been tormented by my lesbianness. In fact, it's a favorite part of me, as Goddess-given as being Black. What I have been tormented by is people's homophobia — their deliberate ignorance concerning my affectional orientation, their active offenses against me because of my sexuality. I am not the problem here: homophobes are.

I'm lesbian — that word is a noun, not an adjective for me — and I notice a good number of other people in this world are also lesbian. I think everyone who is lesbian or a gay male was abused as a child. We were abused because other people didn't want us to be who we were. They tried to twist us into molds unnatural to our selves. We therefore grew up thinking we are bad and everyone around us would jump in and say, "Yes, you're awful and disgusting. Shut up and don't talk about it."

One of the characters in the novel I am working on has these thoughts: "Why should I be the one who was afraid to admit how I was inclined to love, when the Reverend felt so free to proclaim how he hated? Why indeed — because he was empowered by the gumption and gall to hurt me in his anger at the fact that I didn't care to love him. And all the male world would back him up. The female supporters who believed their bounty lay with that male brute force would chorus that he had a perfect right to expect my loyalty, that he was entitled to be the focus of my affections. But that was a lie men enforced for each other and convinced female adherents to believe. I wanted to tell my truth, yet not get smashed to kingdom come for it. So what to do, what to say, how not to give in to the bully, braying in his fear-filled threats before me?"

*****

I've often told the story of discovering myself as a lesbian after reading *The Well of Loneliness* when I was 9 years old. What I want to focus on this time around is hiding.

Despite the sensational words on the covers of the world of lesbian softcover books that I first happened upon with *Summer Camp* by Ann Herbert, and then sought after in drugstores and secondhand bookstores while I was a teenager, I never identified with having a "sordid life," being a "degenerate" nor an "invert." I never felt "unnatural" or trapped in a twisted life as these books' liner notes would tell it.

I wanted to be a lesbian. Somehow I figured book jacket words of condemnation belonged to the point-of-view of a shocked and ignorant heterosexual audience. Even then, I thought the outraged horror just pretense on the heteros' parts, often a lady who "doth protest too much." Wasn't it obvious for all the world to see that some people were queer, just as some people were left-handed, and this is no big deal? But I gleaned that homophobic people were very afraid. I thought that because so many were really mean about it, and people couldn't be that mean without fear.

But I understood, in those 1960s years, that I had to keep my lesbianism secret. I'd read enough books to clue me in to the fact that I'd be perceived as a perverted deviant to heterosexuals who'd profess shock and revulsion towards me if I stated this simple fact of my life. The conventional heterosexer reaction made no sense to me, but I knew it existed. In my teen years I was content to live in a secret sisterhood that had to remain undercover. It seemed my best option.

As I grew from adolescence to teenhood, I never felt a sense of lesbians as being a sick, dangerous, sinful people. I've always liked lesbians — my preferences ran toward the tomboys to butches who "looked like men" to dyke separatists. Lesbians have always been my people and I have ever been glad to identify as one. Nor did any conflict rage in me longing to be straight. This was my normal: to fall in love with girls, to want to

150

be with butch lesbians, to have no more to do with men than a shiny new bicycle would try to mate with a garbage pail.

I knew I couldn't go around shouting this from the rooftops. I'd have to keep my lesbian identity underground and hope to connect with others like me. For that reason, I couldn't wait to get to college, where I fully expected I'd find more lesbians than I could locate in my Brooklyn neighborhood or in high school, where the dykey-looking and dyke-rumored gym teachers gave off straight smoke signals and would not acknowledge me as one of their own.

How I longed for my gym teachers, Miss Kaplan and Mrs. Cohen, to give me a sign. I don't know what I expected — that they wear a tell-tale pinky ring, a green dress every Thursday; that they give me a wink or a significant nod of recognition. Whatever I wanted during my years in Tilden High School, I never got it.

I did glean one girl in the Leaders Gym Club — the sole organization where a teenage girl who was athletically inclined could have any hope of an outlet — who let me touch her. This happened during the bus ride to a Leaders conference. She and I were furtive and never spoke of our — or was it solely my? — hand on her thigh. She had a boyfriend and I had no covers or pretensions. More than feeling driven by sexual desire, I ached to find just one other girl who'd admit to being a lesbian, but no one was letting me in on it at Tilden High.

From the knowledge I got from the books I'd read, I surmised that the other lesbians just didn't know themselves that way yet. But I was noticing what I thought were telling signs and symptoms in my schoolmates. I'd read Jess Stearns' *The Grapevine*,* and I felt certain I recognized latent lesbians. I was biding my time until I got to college, could go to gay bars and from there, fully commence my life as a lesbian.

If it weren't for the books I'd read, I'd have probably come out

---

* *The Grapevine* by Jess Stearns was a pseudo-sociological examination of lesbians done by a male heterosexual journalist who viewed the subject as something titillating and sensational.

a much harder way, and in shame and disgrace. I was spared having a heterosexual homophobe, a latent lesbian or closeted queer shame me with condemnation for being a pervert with unnatural desires. I'd read enough of those scenarios in the lesbian books of softcore porn written to sexually excite men to know the deal. I still thank Goddess for lesbian books. I hope that today the wealth of queer-positive literature will give other lesbian and gay male kids the necessary knowledge of self to know this crucial component of who they are.

My teen years occurred during the era of the shift in race consciousness that moved from "We shall overcome" as good Negroes to "Black Power," its style evidenced by Afro hairstyles and dashikis. I felt uncertain, afraid of and excited by this new Black talk, but at the same time, I feared being called an oreo — Black on the outside, white on the inside — more than I feared being pointed out as a bulldagger.

Nowadays, I get letters from P-FLAG (Parents and Friends of Lesbians and Gays) that are fundraising appeals in the guise of attitude questionnaires. The right answers to the questions are obvious for taking the pulse of homophobia on anyone likely to have an interest in an organization such as P-FLAG. Still, when I read what comes as junk mail, I think back to my adolescence and teenhood, when no such notion of a P-FLAG existed.

The P-FLAG "surveys" ask questions like:

Do you personally know anyone who is lesbian or gay?

Are you comfortable discussing their orientation with them?

Has personally knowing someone who is lesbian or gay changed your ideas about homosexuality?

Do you think information about lesbian women and gay men should be included in appropriate school curricula?

I wish, as if to a galaxy of stars, that my parents could read this stuff — both now and back in my younger years. What a difference it could have made if I had an option other than hiding and sneaking after my secret life. My motivation would not have been for a closer relationship with my family. Rather, I am simply imagining what it could have done for my self-esteem and integrity back then had my parents considered these attitude-challenging questions.

The wise choice for the sake of personal survival in my day

was to remain hidden.

*****

I didn't have a sense that I'd have been disowned by my family or thrown out of the house when I was 16 and engaged in a conversation with my father. Our talk concerned my manner of dressing. As usual, he wanted me to change my clothing style. He was urging me to wear more skirts and dresses when I went to school, rather than wear the pants I so obviously preferred. He exhorted me to adapt a more feminine appearance.

I came as close to cross-dressing as I could during high school. I was 15 in 1968 when the NYC public school system "allowed" girls to wear pants to school. I always chose to wear dungarees, man-tailored shirts, loafers, round-toed sneakers. That was as butch as I dared get.

I recall my father saying, "I fear you're taking on behaviors and attitudes that will stand in the way of having a healthy relationship with men." Well, I took the obvious opening and opportunity to eagerly share with Daddy my joy in the knowledge that I was a lesbian!

His face fell and he faltered from what he saw as an attempt at gentle guidance along the path that he knew best. I saw shock register on the features I most trusted and looked to for approval. My father was my main emotional support and I suddenly wondered if I'd made a serious mistake.

But Daddy didn't launch into a tirade or display of anger. He showed no emotional presence that I can recall. Queer children aren't the only ones who hide around the issue of homosexuality.

One thing I do remember is that he argued for heterosexuality along lines of "... a man has a penis, his hands and a mouth, so there can be no contest about who can satisfy a woman..."

Now I was the one to feel shock — at exactly what I couldn't pin down, but this was not the kind of reaction — self-serving, reactionary, coming from a place way off-base to what I was telling him — that I expected from my liberal, wise, understanding father, a man I believed possessed superior intelligence.

In that moment I realized that my father was not so different

153

from other men after all. He was speaking in anger about sex as if I'd challenged him to a debate about whose technique was better, when I'd ventured to reveal something important about who I was — the way I was inclined to love.

Somehow the conversation did end. I no longer trusted my father to know and be better than most people. I didn't want to risk losing his tenuous approval by bringing up what I knew myself to be. Shortly after that conversation, I went away to college. I never discussed my romantic interests with my father and he never broached the subject of my sexuality.

One reason that gay people come out is to open lines of communication and intimacy, but homophobia closes and kills all possibility of that. For that very reason, when I think of some homophobic individuals, I want to say, "You couldn't be that pissed off without you having some strong involvement. Is the anger at your own desires or at someone you love who is lesbian or homosexual?"

But I've never dared throw down that gauntlet.

*****

Coming out to anyone is frightening, but to family most of all — and family means exposing myself as a lesbian to Black people. Quick, who doesn't quake in fear at the thought of some manner of Black person's moral outrage against lesbians and homosexuals? Lesbians and homosexual men are negatively linked with the evils of white people — "a white man's sickness." Many Blacks take the position of disdaining queerness as far worse than "talking Black and sleeping white" — an attitude which reigned in the days of Black nationalism.

While it is true that there has been a real shift in consciousness about our African heritage and a fuller understanding of how white people have colonized and continue to exploit us, it is also true that postures of Black power have been appliquéd over Black people's very real feelings of victimization. Many proclamations of African-American pride take stances that follow the same oppressive and dehumanizing lines that have been used against Black people. The social structure we live in is so

154

insidious that stances of proud Blackness have been effectively co-opted to sell products that enrich white entrepreneurs moreso than Black ones. Witness commercials urging us to spend money on "Afro Sheen" or "Dark & Lovely" hair care products.

I clearly remember how I avoided heavy Black nationalist groups because I felt I would never pass muster for being Black enough — as a lesbian, as a student at an all-white college, as someone who didn't admire street life or its values, as someone who felt more drawn to "peace and love" than fists and guns for revolution.

I did not want to be around nationalists because of the sexism and homophobia voiced by that movement. Recall Stokely Carmichael's infamous words, "The only place for women in the movement is prone." I felt much more welcome and nurtured by feminism. The women's liberation movement birthed my true coming-of-age politically. I didn't feel Black enough, but feminism and gay liberation embraced social changes I felt were crucial for my survival.

I've seen how men of all stripes have always felt safe to attack lesbians. So often I witness Black women "black-maled" into keeping quiet because we fear being accused as "bulldagger" by Black men. This name-calling from our brothers in oppression seems to me more potent against Black women than for white women, overall.

Along with being keenly aware of the whipping Black men receive from the hands of this society, Black women typically don't fully take into account the lashes applied to ourselves. But we are sensitive to being called too loud, too assertive, aggressive, ball-breaking, domineering matriarchs. Part of racism's insidious legacy is that we buy into these images that are played with a negative spin against us. Furthermore, our brothers have been relentless in using this tool to force Black woman to back down.

So many sisters hear the disdainful, dismissing put-down denial that "lesbianism is a white woman's thing." These women shut themselves up, denying the ever-present lesbianism of Black women, never challenging the assumption of vileness. The call for "unity" has been misused as a club to stifle the wide range of ways of being Black. We must no longer allow anyone to discredit women by calling us "lesbians" in pejorative tones.

*****

We are a community under siege as Black Americans. Lesbi-anism/homosexuality is in some quarters of Black "nationhood" portrayed as a threat to the community. This line of thinking is the place where Black men are clearly in league with white men — to keep the patriarchy in place. The tragedy is that this system of oppression may well be the inroads whereby we can be destroyed as a people.

Homophobic African-Americans at their worst, and I can so easily imagine them in that vein, react to a coming-out disclosure as if you are now something horribly loathsome and supremely disgusting. A significant and tender part of me has no defense against this belief, because I was taught the same line.

However, I now suspect something more telling behind repulsed and judgmental heterosexers' reactions to their imaginings of lesbian sexuality. I sense a horror at any and all sexuality. Heterosex is deemed disgusting enough, but to be a lesbian or homosexual man places you beyond the pale. I think revulsion to sex itself is the fuel running a motor which drives some of the worst homophobes.

For Black people the world over, our sexual nature has been maligned and our sexuality has been the place that white people project their own fears and fantasies. I've never heard whites referring to homosexuality as a particularly Black people's social ill. Perhaps that's why some Black homophobes are so adamant that we not be accused of "queerness" on top of everything else.

Coupled with that, white society expects us to be morally superior, never-ending sources of forgiveness and compassion. That expectation serves to enforce the myth that Blacks are less bedeviled by lesbianism/homosexuality. In many white people's communities, Blacks (and other people of color) are reputed to be more liberal and accepting of homosexuality. I know of that subgroup of white people who find freedom from repression and a refuge for their humanity in the African-American community. I can see the truth to that reality as well.

156

But people in any community of oppression have to understand that differences among us are not grounds for divisions between us. Heterosexual bigots and male-supremacist men have used sexual difference as a reason to exploit and oppress, a weapon to uphold and maintain male advantages over women, leveraging their privilege for power. Lesbians and gay men can't allow this to continue. Audre Lorde wrote in *Sister/Outsider*, "Being an open lesbian in the Black community is not easy, although being closeted is harder."

*****

As I write this in 1995, more people are inclined to mouth phrases of acceptance and welcome my coming-out revelation rather than run away shrieking in horror, shout condemnation or even preach against what they regard as sick sinfulness. Nonetheless, those attitudes still abound.

Note that I said, "mouth phrases of acceptance and welcome." Most people in the general public don't want to be accused of bigotry or called to task on their homophobia. They'll often take pains to mask their true feelings and act weird on you later on down the line. My mother showed me such a face of calm, with slight disappointment, then wrote me a brief letter where she said, "I think you're taking the first step towards cutting your own throat, dear."   Just as it was with coming out to my father, it's hard to remember exactly what happened. I didn't recognize how difficult a rite of passage this coming out business was. I was in my 20s when I told my mother and I still don't fully grasp all the consequences.

I do know my mother wasn't glad for my good fortune to know myself to be a lesbian. I don't think she had any sense that some courage was involved on my part to tell her this truth. She covered up her true reaction, but I could see her retreat to conventional disapproval. I am certain that she didn't try to get any information to educate herself beyond the ideas she already held — negative stereotypes about gay men in the effeminate faggot mold, lesbians entirely unmentionable.

*****

Since my trial-and-error years, I've read numerous articles on coming out and heard speeches encouraging the experience. People spoke of becoming closer to their families and feeling new freedom as their parents transformed from fear-filled dragons to allies on the front lines of P-FLAG.

Not my folks. My mother stayed firmly entrenched in her ignorance, assured that she was right and I was perversely wrong-headed and we wouldn't talk about it. My father kept up his seemingly more liberal front, but neither one of them ever showed an interest in my life as a lesbian. Had I kept myself pink and powdered, I know they would have tried to know more about me.

I wonder if I've been demanding from them what was not their truth?

I did expect more of a response than I got and I didn't have the expertise to pursue what many would consider a child's birth-right. General disappointment and disapproval from my parents was enough to shut me up. Frowning in the background to that rite of passage which gay people see as a courageous and momentous revelation is the societal notion that to be a lesbian or male homosexual is bad and wrong.

Why did I think my parents would react differently or better, or even at all? Partly from reading gay literature with happy-ending coming out stories told about people of a different class and kind than my African-Caribbean-American parents. Maybe I had blind spots from my plain desire that they know and understand me.

After 10 years of my being a vegetarian, my mother had asked at a dinner at her house, "But wouldn't you like some meat, dear?" And after 20 years, my father says, "You're still on that no meat-eating kick?" Lord have mercy.

These are the same people who were surprised when their obviously cross-dressing butch daughter, the offspring who never grew out of being a tomboy, the very child who showed no interest in males as romantic-sexual fodder, told them of her lesbianness.

Would I be aiding and abetting homophobic denial if I explain to other people that my parents are from a different generation, that they are individuals in their 70s now, people who worked as civil servants and thought themselves doing well to have landed "secure city jobs"? Why wasn't it obvious to them, and how could they not have known about me?

I feel both bewildered and skeptical.

Still, I have to factor in that no such notion as therapy as a tool for growth and healing was recognized in their day. Only crazy people went to see psychiatrists, and those crazy individuals were white. Certainly Black people could be driven insane and might be carried to some imagined nuthouse in straitjackets, kicking and screaming all the way. In one of our rare conversations in my adult years, my mother told me that for people in her generation, if you had any kind of difficulties or problems in the family, you went to a priest for guidance.

Now I answer my arguments sadly: What could I expect of them? But then I think, damnit, they watch TV, they read magazines and newspapers. Their ideas can change. They've altered their opinions on other issues.

I remember how I grew up believing I was an ugly kid. I threw away every childhood photo of myself I could find when I was in my teens. Now, I like having pictures taken. I'm pleased with my looks, my beauty and my nonbeauty, but also, and more deeply, I accept my face that I once thought so unattractive. I like my African-Caribbean features. I'm not white and perky. There's no look of "refined European breeding" to me. If Black Americans could have a shift of consciousness to be able to embrace our physical beauty in the face of centuries of being told northern European looks were the standard, then surely my parents and our culture can change outdated ideas about queerness.

I want my family's understanding and appreciation of me. And, I'm still pissed at them. It's been close to 10 years now that I have virtually divorced myself from the family circle. My parents mind their "p's and q's" when I grant an audience once a year. Their light tread on eggshells saves them from having to go too deeply into anything real. But it seems to me that until they grapple with their homophobia, they can't win and neither do I. We all lose.

Letter to Carolyn
by Michelle Wilkinson

You must have been very tired. I wondered if you had fallen asleep waiting for me or if it was your day that was so long and hard. I stood in the doorway watching you while you slept. You were sitting at the desk with your head laying in your folded arms. The church secretary was sitting across from you at her desk watching me watch you. I'm sure she was wondering why I just stood there staring. I motioned for her not to wake you. I wanted to do that myself.

> I wanted. I wanted to kiss you awake. I wanted you to open your eyes and see me right here in front of you. I wanted. I wanted you to know that I was here for you — not for my youth group meeting that started at 6:00 pm, and not for the sermon that my Dad was teaching that night, *but for you.*

* * *

Life was so confusing and very crazy during those days. It seemed that by simply loving you I was tearing my mother's life apart. I was an embarrassment to my family and my father. By loving you I was compromising his position in the church. They were threatening to kick you out of ministerial school. The ministers thought that you were contributing to the delinquency of a minor by taking advantage of me! Little did they know.

Mom kept telling me that it was a phase that we were going through. In her psychoanalysis of the situation, we were both experiencing those schoolgirl crushes that were latent in your 24-year-old mind but prevalent in my 15-year-old one.

I struggled.

I could not understand why everybody was trippin! Somewhere inside of me I knew that we were supposed to be together. I understood it and I knew that it was right. It was just so very hard trying to explain it in a way that would make sense to the

161

people around us.

If I could have opened my heart and opened my head so that they could have seen it and felt it, they would have known that our love was of no harm to me, to you or to their way of life.

I struggled.

Mom said that people did not understand what they were seeing, so in the meantime be discreet. I really did not understand that. How do you discreetly love someone? I wanted to ask them how could I hide my love for you when all I wanted to do was to scream from the highest mountain that I finally found the love that I was looking for?

I struggled.

I knew that God and I were on pretty good terms. We walked and talked together. We had an understanding. So I knew that when I asked if loving you was wrong, if this was not God's will that I would be led in the right direction.

* * *

It's rather ironic. I'm sure my father never knew that he led me right to the answer in a lesson he taught that Sunday in church, "What is God's Will?". I learned that God's will was for us to love ourselves and to love each other. I realized that my mother was right. People did not understand what they were seeing. They could not understand the love that we were sharing. I knew that I was a good person. I loved people. I gave of myself and I only wished the best for those around me. I sure wasn't going to make their problems my problem. My mother had always instilled a high sense of self-esteem in her children!

You know, we were lucky. We discovered each other at a time when we were surrounded by church-going women-lovin-women who were waiting for us to take our baby-dyke steps out of the closet into our lives. They watched out for us as we stumbled through this life we were intended to lead. We found strength in Shernita, Kay, Becky and many others, and we knew that we were not alone.

I also feel fortunate that my parents were willing to grow with us. They made you part of our family. I think they realized that it was a lot easier to gain a daughter than to lose one.

* * *

It was funny. I did walk over and kiss you on the forehead.

You jumped up, completely startled, and hit me square on the nose with your head.

It was comical. The church secretary laughed. I think we all laughed.

But afterward you told me that you were dreaming. And in your dream it was me you were waiting for.

Long Way Home
by Tiffani Frazier

When I was very little,
Preschool age, in fact,
I had my first "girlfriend."
Her name was Keisha
And she was a beautiful little dark brown girl.
She was smooth chocolate, just like me.
I loved to tickle her
Because her smile lit up my world
I loved to put my chubby hand on her cheek
     And look long into her eyes and kiss her.

It felt natural and right.

Then on one snowy evening when I was six,
I walked with my mother to the corner paperstand.
But this time I was noticing the magazines inside.
And some of them had pictures of naked womyn
     With the smoothest looking skin on the covers.
I was mesmerized. I was hypnotized. I couldn't
     take my eyes off these womyn.
I was Turned On.

But then I did the unthinkable.
Not knowing what any of this meant, an innocent
     six-year-old girl asked her neo-Fundamentalist
     Christian mother to buy some of those
     magazines for her daughter.

165

My mother gave me the most horrified look
    I've ever seen, like in the painting "The Silent
    Scream."
She didn't breathe a word — just looked at me
    like I was no longer her daughter but a
    terrible, grotesque creature.
She tightly grabbed my arm and dragged me across
    the street so fast that my feet could barely
    keep up with her.

That's when I knew that a girl who likes other girls
    is unacceptable.
But not just unacceptable, IMMORAL. WRONG.
SHOULD NOT EXIST.

So I worked really hard to get interested in boys
    because I wanted Mom to love me; she's the
    only family I've ever had and I wanted her
    to be proud of me.

Throughout Catholic school and high school, I still
    disliked boys: I didn't like their macho
    attitudes and I certainly didn't like their bodies.
    I still (carefully) looked at the girls with the
    rounding hips and the full lips. Mmmmm....
But I kept all of this to myself and TOLD NO ONE.
I played along. I was miserable.
Mom was happy, though. I guess she figured,
    "Hey, she may not have a boyfriend but she
    doesn't have a girlfriend, either."

166

That is, not until my roaring twenties.

1990 came along and everywhere I looked,
       people were popping out of the closet and
       talking on TV. About being Lesbian and gay.
All sorts of books were getting published and
       people were discussing their experiences with
       "the lifestyle."
They were open about their joys, as well as their
       pains from harassment.
And then I noticed the same theme running
       through all these stories: being honest is freeing.
Lying to yourself is like being trapped in a cave.

That's when I adopted my own personal motto:
       NEW DECADE + NEW ATTITUDE =
         IT'S TIME TO TELL MOM

I knew I had to tell her because, to me, living a
       lie is like living on the run. The hiding had
       to stop. And the opportunity just fell in my
       living room one afternoon.

Mom was in the kitchen and I was up front in
the living room with my trusty remote in hand,
channel surfing. I found "Donahue" and the topic
was "Coming Out as Lesbian and Gay." I started
watching and PRAYED that Mom would wander into
the room. When she did, she was watching the show
with me, silently. I began agreeing with what one

of the speakers was saying. Then my mother looked
at me and said,
     "Why are you agreeing with him?"
     "Because I've read his book."
     "Why aren't you reading heterosexual books?"
     "Because I'm not heterosexual." I sounded firm
and calm but inside I was shaky as hell.

I honestly don't remember what happened next.

But in the ensuing weeks, she went through
     MASSIVE denial then MASSIVE anger which
     she expressed by not speaking to me for
     a couple of months. The silence was deafening.

A few months after that, I surrendered and found
     a man at my place of work to "date." Mother
     was no doubt very pleased and wanted to know
     all about him.
But that little "affair," of course, lasted about two
     secônds and then I met this very pretty
     Black woman. She had an uncanny resemblance
     to my little Keisha from preschool: same eyes,
     same dimples, same smile.
I was very quickly smitten with her and I didn't
     bother to hide our phone conversations from my
     mother. I was answering my true calling and
     just didn't give a shit anymore. I was "out."

This "third" coming out proved not to be so charming

for my mother as I could not and would not
lie to her about my true orientation. And
did she make me pay dearly for it.
Endless screaming, endless fighting. She
attempted to hit me on more than one
occasion. But to no avail — I refused to back
down and for that she soon kicked me out
so I'd no longer contaminate her home. I
think that was the worst year of my life.

Nowadays, I share an apartment and work as a
cashier and I'm trying to get back in school.
I've been gone from home for more than a
year and have spoken with my mother on
maybe 10 very brief occasions. We haven't
spoken with each other for the last three
months or so because I refuse to deal with
her only on her terms. To her, she is always
"The Parent" and I'm always "the child."
Being recognized as an adult with feelings
and concerns is very important to me. She
won't give me that. I'm not sure if she can.

So every day I try to stay free and maintain
my dear family of friends the best way I know how.

Man Royals and Sodomites: Some Thoughts on the Invisibility of Afro-Caribbean Lesbians
by Makeda Silvera

I will begin with some personal images and voices about
woman-loving. These have provided a ground for my search for
cultural reflections of my identity as a Black woman artist within
the Afro-Caribbean community of Toronto. Although I focus
here on my own experience (specifically, Jamaican), I am aware
of similarities with the experience of other Third World women
of colour whose history and culture has been subjected to
colonisation and imperialism.

I spent the first thirteen years of my life in Jamaica among
strong women. My great-grandmother, my grandmother and
grand-aunts were major influences in my life. There are also men
whom I remember with fondness — my grandmother's "man
friend" G., my Uncle Bertie, his friend Paul, Mr. Minott, Uncle
B. and Uncle Freddy. And there were men like Mr. Eden who
terrified me because of his stories about his "walking" fingers
and his liking for girls under age fourteen.

I lived in a four-bedroom house with my grandmother, Uncle
Bertie and two female tenants. On the same piece of land, my
grandmother had other tenants, mostly women and lots of
children. The big verandah of our house played a vital role in the
social life of this community. It was on the verandah that I
received my first education on "Black women's strength" — not
only from their strength, but also from the daily humiliations
they bore at work and in relationships. European experience
coined the term "feminism," but the term "Black women's
strength" reaches beyond Eurocentric definitions to describe
what is the cultural continuity of my own struggles.

The verandah. My grandmother sat on the verandah in the
evenings after all the chores were done to read the newspaper.
People — mostly women — gathered there to discuss "life." Life
covered every conceivable topic — economic, local, political,
social and sexual: the high price of salt-fish, the scarcity of flour,

the nice piece of yellow yam bought at Coronation market, Mr. Lam, the shopkeeper who was taking "liberty" with Miss Inez, the fights women had with their menfolk, work, suspicions of Miss Iris and Punsie carrying on something between them, the cost of school books...

My grandmother usually had lots of advice to pass on to the women on the verandah, all grounded in the Bible. Granny believed in Jesus, in good and evil and in repentance. She was also a practical and sociable woman. Her faith didn't interfere with her perception of what it meant to be a poor Black woman; neither did it interfere with our Friday night visits to my Aunt Marie's bar. I remember sitting outside on the piazza with my grandmother, two grand-aunts and three or four of their women friends. I liked their flashy smiles and I was fascinated by their independence, ease and their laughter. I loved their names — Cherry Rose, Blossom, Jonesie, Poinsietta, Ivory, Pearl, Iris, Bloom, Dahlia, Babes. Whenever the conversation came around to some "big 'oman talk" — who was sleeping with whom or whose daughter just got "fallen" — I was sent off to get a glass of water for an adult, or a bottle of Kola champagne. Every Friday night I drank as much as half a dozen bottles of Kola champagne, but I still managed to hear snippets of words, tail ends of conversations about women together.

In Jamaica, the words used to describe many of these women would be "Man Royal" and/or "Sodomite." Dread words. So dread that women dare not use these words to name themselves. They were names given to women by men to describe aspects of our lives that men neither understood nor approved.

I heard "sodomite" whispered a lot during my primary school years, and tales of women secretly having sex, joining at the genitals, and being taken to the hospital to be "cut" apart were told in the school yard. Invariably, one of the women would die. Every five to ten years the same story would surface. At times, it would even be published in the newspapers. Such stories always generated much talking and speculation from "Bwoy dem kinda gal naasti sah!" to some wise old woman saying, "But dis caan happen, after two shutpan caan join" — meaning identical objects cannot go into the other. The act of loving someone of the same sex was sinful, abnormal — something to hide. Even today, it isn't unusual or uncommon to be asked, "So how do two 'omen do it? ...what unnu use for a penis? ...who is the man and who is the 'oman?" It's inconceivable that women can have intimate relationships that are whole, that are not lacking because of the absence of a man. It's assumed that women in such relationships must be imitating men.

The word "sodomite" derives from the Old Testament. Its common use to describe lesbians (or any strong independent woman) is peculiar to Jamaica — a culture historically and strongly grounded in the Bible. Although Christian values have dominated the world, their effect in slave colonies is particular. Our foreparents gained access to literacy through the Bible when they were being indoctrinated by missionaries. It provided powerful and ancient stories of strength, endurance and hope which reflected their own fight against oppression. This book has been so powerful that it continues to bind our lives with its racism and misogyny. Thus, the importance the Bible plays in Afro-Caribbean culture must be recognised in order to understand the historical and political context for the invisibility of lesbians. The wrath of God "rained down burning sulphur on Sodom and Gomorrah" *(Genesis 19:23)*. How could a Caribbean woman claim the name?

When, thousands of miles away and fifteen years after my school days, my grandmother was confronted with my love for a woman, her reaction was determined by her Christian faith and by this dread word sodomite — its meaning, its implication, its history.

And when, Bible in hand, my grandmother responded to my love by sitting me down, at the age of twenty-seven, to quote Genesis, it was within the context of this tradition, this politic. When she pointed out that "this was a white people ting," or "a ting only people with mixed blood was involved in" (to explain or include my love with a woman of mixed race), it was strong denial of many ordinary Black working-class women she knew.

It was finally through my conversations with my grandmother, my mother and my mother's friend five years later that I began to realise the scope of this denial which was intended to dissuade and protect me. She knew too well that any woman who took a woman lover was attempting to walk on fire — entering a

173

"no man's land." I began to see how commonplace the act of loving women really was, particularly in working-class communities. I realised, too, just how heavily shame and silence weighed down this act.

A conversation with a friend of my mother:

Well, when I growing up we didn't hear much 'bout woman and woman. They weren't "suspect." There was much more talk about "batty man business" when I was a teenager in the 1950s.

I remember one story about a man who was "suspect" and that every night when he was coming home, a group of guys use to lay wait him and stone him so viciously that he had to run for his life. Dem time, he was safe only in the day.

Now with women, nobody really suspected. I grew up in the country and I grew up seeing women holding hands, hugging up, sleeping together in one bed and there was no question. Some of this was based purely on emotional friendship, but I also knew of cases where the women were dealing but no one really suspected. Close people around knew, but not everyone. It wasn't a thing that you would go out and broadcast. It would be something just between the two people.

Also one important thing is that the women who were involved carried on with life just the same, no big political statements were made. These women still went to church, still got baptised, still went on pilgrimage, and I am thinking about one particular woman name Aunt Vie, a very strong woman, strong-willed and everything, they use to call her "man royal" behind her back, but no one ever dare to meddle with her.

Things are different now in Jamaica. Now all you have to do is not respond to a man's call to you and dem call you sodomite or lesbian. I guess it was different back then forty years ago because it was harder for anybody to really conceive of two woman sleeping and being sexual. But I do remember when you were "suspect," people would talk about you. You were definitely classed as "different," "not normal," a bit "crazy." But women never really got stoned like the men.

What I remember is that if you were a single woman alone or two single women living together and a few people suspected this ... and when I say a few people I mean like a few guys, sometimes other crimes were committed against the women. Some very violent, some very subtle. Battery was common, especially in Kingston. A group of men would suspect a woman or have it out for her because she was a "sodomite" or because she act "man royal" and so the men would organise and gang rape whichever woman was "suspect." Sometimes it was reported in the newspapers, other times it wasn't — but when you live in a little community, you don't need a newspaper to tell you what's going on. You know by word of mouth and those stories were frequent. Sometimes you also knew the men who did the battery.

Other subtle forms of this was "scorning" the women. Meaning that you didn't eat anything from them, especially a cooked meal. it was almost as if those accused of being "man royal" or "sodomite" could contaminate.

A conversation with my grandmother:

I am telling you this so that you can understand that this is not a profession to be proud of and to get involved in. Everybody should be curious and I know you born with that, ever since you growing up as a child and I can't fight against that, because that is how everybody get to know what's in the world. I am only telling you this because when you were a teenager, you always say you want to experience everything and make up your mind on your own. You didn't like people telling you what was wrong and right. That always use to scare me.

Experience is good, yes. But it have to be balanced, you have to know when you have too much experience in one area. I am telling you this because I think you have enough experience in this to decide now to go back to the normal way. You have two children. Do you want them to grow up knowing this is the life you have taken? But this is for you to decide...

Yes, there was a lot of women involved with women in Jamaica. I knew a lot of them when I was growing up in the country in the 1920s. I didn't really associate with them. Mind you, I was not rude to them. My mother wouldn't stand for any rudeness from any of her children to adults.

175

I remember a woman we use to call Miss Bibi. She live next to us — her husband was a fisherman, I think he drowned before I was born. She had a little wooden house that back onto the sea, the same as our house. She was quiet, always reading. That I remember about her because she use to go to the little public library at least four days out of the week. And she could talk. Anything you want to know, just ask Miss Bibi and she could tell you. She was a mulatto woman, but poor. Anytime I had any school work that I didn't understand, I use to ask her. The one thing I remember though, we wasn't allowed in her house by my mother, so I use to talk to her outside, but she didn't seem to mind that. Some people use to think she was mad because she spent so much time alone. But I didn't think that because anything she help me with, I got a good mark on it in school.

She was colourful in her own way, but quiet, always alone, except when her friend come and visit her once a year for two weeks. Them times I didn't see Miss Bibi much because my mother told me I couldn't go and visit her. Sometimes I would see her in the market exchanging and bartering fresh fish for vegetables and fruits. I use to see her friend too. She was a jet Black woman, always had her hair tied in bright coloured cloth and she always had on big gold earrings. People use to say she live on the other side of the island with her husband and children and she came to Port Maria once a year to visit Miss Bibi.

My mother and father were great storytellers and I learnt that from them, but is from Miss Bibi that I think I learnt to love reading so much as a child. It wasn't until I move to Kingston that I notice other women like Miss Bibi...

Let me tell you about Jones. Do you remember her? Well she was the woman who live the next yard over from us. She is the one who really turn me against people like that, why I fear so much for you to be involved in this ting. She was very loud. Very show-off. Always dressed in pants and man-shirt that she borrowed from her husband. Sometimes she use to invite me over to her house, but I didn't go. She always had her hair in a bob hair cut, always barefoot and tending to her garden and her fruit trees. She tried to get me involved in that kind of life, but I said no. At the time I remember I needed some money to borrow and she lent me, later she told me I didn't have to pay her back, but to come over to her house and see the thing she had that was sweeter than what any man could offer me. I told her no and eventually paid her back the money.

We still continued to talk. It was hard not to like Jonesie — that's what everybody called her. She was open and easy to talk to. But still there was a fear in me about her. To me it seem like she was in a dead end with nowhere to go. I don't want that for you.

I left my grandmother's house that day feeling anger and sadness for Miss Jones — maybe for myself, who knows. I was feeling boxed in. I had said nothing. I'd only listened quietly.

In bed that night, I thought about Miss Jones. I cried for her (for me) silently. I remember her, a mannish looking Indian woman, with flashy gold teeth, a Craven A cigarette always between them. She was always nice to me as a child. She had the sweetest, juiciest Julie, Bombay and East Indian mangoes on the street. She always gave me mangoes over the fence. I remember the dogs in her yard and the sign on her gate. "Beware of bad dogs." I never went into her house, though I was always curious.

I vaguely remember her pants and shirts, though I never thought anything about them until my grandmother pointed them out. Neither did I recall that dreaded word being used to describe her, although everyone on the street knew about her.

A conversation with my mother:

Yes I remember Miss Jones. She smoke a lot, drank a lot. In fact, she was an alcoholic. When I was in my teens she use to come over to our house — always on the verandah. I can't remember her sitting down — seems like she was always standing up, smoking, drinking and reminiscing. She constantly talked about the past, about her life and it was always on the verandah. And it was always women: young women she knew when she was a young woman, the fun they had together and how good she would make love to a woman. She would say to whoever was listening on the verandah, "Dem girls I use to have sex with was shapely. You shoulda know me when I was younger, pretty and shapely just like the 'oman dem I use to have

177

as my 'oman."

People use to tease her on the street, but not about being a lesbian or calling her a sodomite. People use to tease her when she was drunk, because she would leave the rumshop and stagger down the avenue to her house.

I remember the women she use to carry home, usually in the daytime. A lot of women from downtown, higglers and fishwomen. She use to boast about knowing all kinds of women from Coronation market and her familiarity with them. She had a husband who lived with her and that served as her greatest protection against other men taking steps with her. Not that anybody could easily take advantage of Miss Jones, she could stand up for herself. But having a husband did help. He was a very quiet, insular man. He didn't talk to anyone on the street. He had no friends so it wasn't easy for anyone to come up to him and gossip about his wife.

No one could go to her house without being invited, but I wouldn't say she was a private person. She was a loner. She went to the rumshops alone, she drank alone, she staggered home alone. The only time I ever saw her with somebody were the times when she went off to Coronation market or some other place downtown to find a woman and bring her home. The only times I remember her engaging in conversation with anybody was when she came over to the verandah to talk about her women and what they did in bed. That was all she let out about herself. There was nothing about how she was feeling, whether she was sad or depressed, lonely, happy. Nothing. She seemed to cover up all that with her loudness and her vulgarness and her constant threat — which was all it was — to beat up anybody who troubled her or teased her when she was coming home from the rumshop.

Now Cherry Rose — do you remember her? She was a good friend of Aunt Marie's and of Mama's. She was also a sodomite. She was loud too, but different from Miss Jones. She was much more outgoing. She was a barmaid and had lots of friends — both men and women. She also had the kind of personality that attracted people — very vivacious, always laughing, talking and touching. She didn't have any children, but Gem did.

Do you remember Miss Gem? Well she had children and she

178

was also a barmaid. She also had lots of friends She also had a man friend name Mickey, but that didn't matter because some women had their men and still had women they carried on with. The men usually didn't know what was going on, and seeing as these men just come and go and usually on their own time, they weren't around every day and night.

Miss Pearl was another one that was in that kind of thing. She was a dressmaker, she use to sew really good. Where Gem was light complexion, she was a very Black woman with deep dimples. Where Gem was a bit plump, Pearl was slim, but with big breast and a big bottom. The were both pretty women.

I don't remember hearing that word sodomite a lot about them. It was whispered sometimes behind their backs, but never in front of them. And they were so alive and talkative that people were always around them.

The one woman I almost forgot was Miss Opal, a very quiet woman. She use to be friends with Miss Olive and was always out at her bar sitting down. I can't remember much about her except she didn't drink like Miss Jones and she wasn't vulgar. She was soft-spoken, a half-Chinese woman. Her mother was born in Hong Kong and her father was a Black man. She could really bake. She use to supply shops with cakes and other pastries.

So there were many of those kind of women around. But it wasn't broadcast.

I remembered them. Not as lesbians or sodomites or man royals, but as women that I liked. Women who I admired. Strong women, some colourful, some quiet.

I loved Cherry Rose's style. I loved her loudness, the way she challenged men in arguments, the bold way she laughed in their faces, the jingle of her gold bracelets. Her colourful and stylish way of dressing. She was full of wit; words came alive in her mouth.

Miss Gem: I remember her big double iron bed. That was where Paula and Lorraine (her daughters, my own age) and I spent a whole week together when we had chicken pox. My grandmother took me there to stay for the company. It was fun. Miss Gem lived right above her bar and so at any time we could look through the window and onto the piazza and street which was bursting with energy and life. She was a very warm woman, patient and caring. Every day she would make soup for us and tell us stories. Later on in the evening she would bring us Kola champagne.

Miss Pearl sewed dresses for me. She hardly ever used her tape measure — she could just take one look at you and make you a dress fit for a queen. What is she doing now, I asked myself? And Miss Opal, with her calm and quiet, where is she — still baking?

What stories could these lesbians have told us? I, an Afro-Caribbean woman living in Canada, come with this baggage — their silenced stories. My grandmother and mother know the truth, but silence still surrounds us. The truth remains a secret to the rest of the family and friends, and I must decide whether to continue to sew this cloth of denial or break free, creating and becoming the artist that I am, bring alive the voices and images of Cherry Rose, Miss Gem, Miss Jones, Opal, Pearl, and others...

There is more at risk for us than for white women. Through three hundred years of history we have carried memories and the scars of racism and violence with us. We are the sister, daughter, mothers of a people enslaved by colonialists and imperialists. Under slavery, production and reproduction were inextricably linked. Reproduction served not only to increase the labour force of slave owners but also, by "domesticating" the enslaved, facilitated the process of social conditions by focusing on those aspects of life in which they could express their own desires. Sex was an area in which to articulate one's humanity, but, because it was tied to attempts "to define oneself as human," gender roles, as well as the act of sex, became badges of status. To be male was to be the stud, the procreator; to be female was to be fecund, and one's femininity was measured by the ability to attract and hold a man, and to bear children. In this way, slavery and the post-emancipated colonial order defined the structures of patriarchy and heterosexuality as necessary for social mobility and acceptance.

Socio-economic conditions and the quest for a better life has seen steady migration from Jamaica and the rest of the Caribbean to the U.S., Britain and Canada. Upon my arrival, I became a part of the so-called "visible minorities" encompassing Blacks, Asians and Native North Americans in Canada. I live with a legacy of continued racism and prejudice. We confront this daily, both as individuals and as organised political groups. Yet for those of us who are lesbians, there is another struggle: the struggle for acceptance and positive self-definition within our own communities. Too often, we have had to sacrifice our love for women in political meetings that have been dominated by the "we are the world" attitude of heterosexual ideology. We have had to hide too often that part of our identity which contributes profoundly to make up the whole.

Many lesbians have worked, like me, in the struggles of Black people since the 1960s. We have been on marches every time one of us gets murdered by the police. We have been at sit-ins and vigils. We have flyered, postered, we have cooked and baked for the struggle. We have tended to the youths. And we have all at one time or another given support to men in our community, all the time painfully holding onto, obscuring, our secret lives. When we do walk out of the closet (or are thrown out), the "ideologues" of the Black community say "Yes, she was a radical sistren but, I don't know what happen, she just went the wrong way." What is implicit in this is that one cannot be a lesbian and continue to do political work, and not surprisingly, it follows that a Black lesbian/artist cannot create using the art forms of our culture. For example, when a heterosexual male friend came to my house, I put on a dub poetry tape. He asked, "Are you sure that sistren is a lesbian?"

"Why?" I ask.

"Because this poem sound wicked; it have lots of rhythm; it sounds cultural."

Another time, another man commented on my work, "That book you wrote on domestic workers is really a fine piece of work. I didn't know you were that informed about the economic politics of the Caribbean and Canada." What are we to assume from this? That Afro-Caribbean lesbians have no Caribbean culture? That they lose their community politics when they sleep with women? Or that Afro-Caribbean culture is a heterosexual commodity?

The presence of an "out" Afro-Caribbean lesbian in our

181

community is dealt with by suspicion and fear from both men and our heterosexual Black sisters. It brings into question the assumption of heterosexuality as the only "normal" way. It forces them to acknowledge something that has always been covered up. It forces them to look at women differently and brings into question the traditional Black female role. Negative response from our heterosexual Black sister, though more painful, is, to a certain extent, understandable because we have no race privilege and very, very few of us have class privilege. The one privilege within our group is heterosexual. We have all suffered at the hands of this racist system at one time or another and to many heterosexual Black women it is inconceivable, almost frightening, that one could turn her back on credibility in our community and the society at large by being lesbian. These women are also afraid that they will be labeled "lesbian" by association. It is that fear, that homophobia, which keeps Black women isolated.

The Toronto Black community has not dealt with sexism. It has not been pushed to do so. Neither has it given a thought to its heterosexism. In 1988, my grandmother's fear is very real, very alive. One takes a chance when one writes about being an Afro-Caribbean lesbian. There is the fear that one might not live to write more. There is the danger of being physically "disciplined" for speaking as a woman-identified woman.

And what of our white lesbian sisters and their community? They have learnt well from the civil rights movement about organising, and with race and some class privilege, they have built a predominantly white lesbian (and gay) movement — a precondition for a significant body of work by a writer or artist. They have demanded and received recognition from politicians (no matter how little). But this recognition has not been extended to Third World lesbians of colour — neither from politicians nor from white lesbian (and gay) organisations. The white lesbian organisations/groups have barely (some not at all) begun to deal with or acknowledge their own racism, prejudice and biases — all learned from a system which feeds on their ignorance and grows stronger from its institutionalised racism. Too often white women focus only on their oppression as lesbians, ignoring the more complex oppression of non-white women who are also

182

lesbians. We remain outsiders in these groups, without images or political voices that echo our own. We know too clearly that, as non-white lesbians in this country, we are politically and socially at the very bottom of the heap. Denial of such differences robs us of true visibility. We must identify and define these differences, and challenge the movements and groups that are not accessible to non-whites — challenge groups that are not accountable.

But where does this leave us as Afro-Caribbean lesbians, as part of the "visible minority" community? As Afro-Caribbean women we are still at the stage where we have to imagine and discover our existence, past and present. As lesbians, we are even more marginalised, less visible. The absence of a national Black lesbian and gay movement through which to begin to name ourselves is disheartening. We have no political organisation to support us and through which we could demand respect from our communities. We need such an organisation to represent our interests, both in coalition-building with other lesbian/gay organisations, and in the struggles which shape our future — through which we hope to transform the social, political and economic systems of oppression as they affect all peoples.

Though not yet on a large scale, lesbians and gays of Caribbean descent are beginning to seek each other out — are slowly organising. Younger lesbians and gays of colour are beginning to challenge and force their parents and the Black community to deal with their sexuality. They have formed groups, "Zami for Black and Caribbean gays and lesbians" and "Lesbians of Colour," to name two.

The need to make connections with other Caribbean and Third World people of colour who are lesbian and gay is urgent. This is where we can begin to build that other half of our community, to create wholeness through our art. This is where we will find the support and strength to struggle, to share our histories and to record these histories in books, documentaries, film, sound, and art. We will create a rhythm that is uniquely ours — proud, powerful and gay, naming ourselves, and taking our space within the larger history of Afro-Caribbean peoples.

Mavis writes in her journal
by Cheryl Clarke

. . . I know Geneva loves me
more than the man she sleeps with every night
and still our conversation is reduced
from talk of world events to
news of the latest white sale
whenever he blunders into the kitchen
for a toothpick.

. . . Geneva can't tell him the same secrets she tells me. . . .

He draws the blood. I know the scars. I acknowledge her mind.
He ignores her body and makes her sense a dartboard.

. . . Why is it we never act on our own hunger?

Yesterday we were listening to Billie Holiday sing
'Do Your Duty' when Geneva lost track of time, rushed home to cook
his dinner. . . . Men learn to be chefs and short order cooks
but never learn to feed themselves.

. . . I am patient and relentless.

Today I kissed Geneva square on the lips and today for the first time
she asked me to leave when he came home from work and went straight
to the icebox for a beer, grunting at us as he popped the cap, exploding
the contents all over Geneva's highly polished linoleum.

. . . Our touches were tentative at first, then there was confidence,
and passion, and wonder . . . then fear.

. . . He's too sure of his cock ever to suspect it will be supplanted.
Tonight Geneva keeps him company.
Tonight I write another brazen love poem in secret, alone, patient,
and relentless.

Me, Growing Up, (part 1)
by Letta Neely

Now me, I have loved womyn intrinsically
like I love blackness and collard greens
like i feel the rhythm of double dutch inside my marrow

I remember the summer when I was nine, climbing
trees and loving shaney
like little girls can love each other
we played softball and basketball on alternatingdays
nights,
we learned what felt good to nine year old bodies

That summer it wouldn't have mattered if a winter storm
had descended upon us
daybreak always found us naked and rushing
to put on clothes
before nana or mama walked in

That summer I was in love
with books
in love with climbing trees and softball
and touching shaney's body
kissing her lips softly
there were times when we'd be wrestling and
have to stop because my heart/her heart would
start pounding
then she would lay on
top of
me and move back and
forth
back and forth
and both our eyes
would be
wide open
daring each other
to laugh

Miss Ruth
by Terri Jewell

Ruth Ellis is a 90+-year-old Black lesbian presently living in
Detroit, Michigan. Conversations were held with her on April 23,
1989 in Lansing, Michigan and on February 10, 1990 in Detroit.

RUTH ELLIS: My life has been nothing special. I am a quiet
person who came from a very ordinary, middle-class Negro
family. I was born July 23, 1899 in Springfield, Illinois. My
Dad's name was Charles Sr. He was a stately-looking man, like
what I would call a Black colonel. I favor him. My Daddy was a
well-built man and black-skinned. Very proud. I don't think he
had much schooling, but he knew what it was all about. I didn't
appreciate him when I was younger like I think I could now. I
sort of feared him. He was so strict, you know. And I shied away
from him. I clung to my mother. Her name was Carrie Farrell.
She was very smooth. Just a kind person. I was crazy about her.
My mother was medium-brown, a nice-looking woman. I was a
"Momma's girl." I have my birth certificate ...

TERRI JEWELL: Your mother was 35 years old when you
were born and she was from Tennessee, as was your father. He
was 38 when you were born. She was a housewife and he was a
mail carrier.

ELLIS: I do remember my mother saying something about
being born in, she'd say, "in '65." I think she must have been in
her 40s when she died. She had a massive stroke and I was
around 11 or 12 years old. My daddy raised us children.
I had three brothers. Wellington was the youngest brother.
Harry was the middle one and Charles Jr., the oldest. I was the
baby, and had a twin who died as a baby. All my brothers were
WWI veterans. Harry and Charles Jr. went overseas but not
Wellington. He eventually got married. Now, my oldest brother
never married. I think Charles Jr. was gay. He never talked about
it or anything like that. Harry never married but became a doctor.

189

We had quite a bit of music in our family. My Daddy used to sing in the choir at St. Paul AME in Springfield and my brother played the pipe organ. The oldest brother could play the violin. The middle brother played piano and the youngest brother played drums. I played mandolin and could play piano by ear, but I didn't get very far with any of it. I like the better class of music — orchestra music and the old-fashioned religious music like Marian Anderson sang. And we played jazz and dance music. I love to dance. I don't know too much about this modern music at all. I don't listen to it at all except when I go dancing. But I don't like the records I hear these days. I don't like vulgarity.

We lived in an integrated neighborhood in Springfield. There was a riot there when I was 8 years old. The whites rioted because they found out a Black man had a white wife. White people were told to put sheets up in their windows so the rioters would burn out only Black families. The only weapon my Daddy had was a sword from the Knights of Pythias.* Troops came in and took all the weapons away from the colored people but not the whites. The wrong Black man was hung. I didn't even know what a riot was.

I do remember one friend I used to have. She was a white girl named Esther Black. My mother would let me go down the block to play with Esther for a half-hour. And Mrs. Black would let Esther come over my house and play, too. When we started school, though, we could play together anymore. When children are left alone, they don't care about all the foolishness that the parents worry over. Children get all that hate from their parents.

I didn't learn too much when I was in school. If I were going to school now, I would be in what you would call "special classes" because I was a slow learner. I went to a white school. They didn't pay attention to colored kids then. I had no one to take a real interest in my schoolwork. My brothers, I guess, were busy studying for themselves. My daddy was crazy about schooling. We had a little library and he had the works of

---

* Knights of Pythias — members of a secret benevolent and fraternal order.

Shakespeare, a set of encyclopedias and law books.

We could go into the theaters, but we had to sit in what they called "Pigeon Heaven" — way up in the balcony. We couldn't go in the restaurants. We couldn't go to the "Y" where young white kids could learn to swim. We had to go to the river to learn to swim. But Daddy wouldn't let us go everyday because too many children got drowned.

But the teachers didn't teach me anything, you know? Now, if I had been raised in the South as a kid, I would have been taught to work. I was a loner in school. I didn't mix very well with the white girls. Or they didn't mix with me. In gym class, the teacher would have to hold my hand because some of the girls didn't want to hold hands with someone Black.

When I went to high school, I fell in love with my gym teacher. She was a Portuguese woman named Grace L., and it didn't matter to her what color anyone was. I didn't get through Springfield High School.

JEWELL: Were you gay before you were 21 years old?

ELLIS: Yes. I used to fool around with girls and have them stay all night. One morning, my Daddy said, "Next time ya'll make that much noise, I'm going to put you BOTH out."

JEWELL: You mean to tell me you were in your daddy's house?!!!

ELLIS: Sure! That's where I lived! I think he was kind of glad I had a woman instead of a man because he was afraid I'd come up with a baby. If you had a baby in those days, you'd have to leave home. And he wanted me home.

I've had one intimate boyfriend. He took me to Decatur to a dance and that was something! Then, all of a sudden, I never saw him again. And I know what happened. The people he stayed with knew I was gay. "You with a bulldagger ..." And I never saw that fellow again. He has passed [away] now.

My people have been dead so long, so long. Daddy was the first colored man to be at the post office in Springfield, Illinois. A man insulted him once and Daddy got fired. He never got a good job after that.

JEWELL: What kinds of jobs have you worked?

ELLIS: Just printing. After the war, my oldest brother, Charles, came to Detroit. I left Springfield when I was 37 and moved to Detroit because Charles was here. Now, when I first started to work in Springfield, I made $3 a week taking care of a baby and I stayed on the place. The top wage then was $10 a week. If you were a cook, you got top wages. But look at what you could get with $10, with $3!! You could buy 2 cents worth of potatoes, a steak for 15 cents, a loaf of bread for a nickel. You could buy a penny's worth of candy, your insurance would be 5 cents a week — a "5-cent policy." When I moved to Detroit, I got a job making $7 a week. In the meantime, on Thursdays I would look for a printing job. I finally found one and stayed there about 10 years.

JEWELL: But how did you get interested in printing?

ELLIS: Well, I kind of fell into it. After high school in Springfield, a neighborhood man taught me how to set type and run his presses. I stayed with him for quite awhile. When I moved to Detroit, I worked for a printer named Waterfield for awhile, then decided to have a shop of my own.

I had one real girlfriend. Her name was Ceciline. We called her Babe. She was the only person I had ever lived with. Babe was from Springfield and she once told me, "If you ever leave Springfield, I'll come where you are." So, when I came to Detroit, she came here too, but later. WE lived together for 30 years. Babe was 10 years younger than I and weighed about 250 pounds, stood under 5'5". And she was medium-brown. She could cook! That she could do. And she always wore a dress.

When I decided to have a shop of my own, my girlfriend and I bought a home. It was a two-family flat at 10335 Oakland Avenue in Detroit. There were 5 rooms downstairs and I took the front room for my shop. I printed anything small, not books or things like that where it had to be Linotyped. I did all printing by hand. The largest printing I did was 11" x 14". I called it "Ellis and Franklin Printing Company." I didn't have any help, either.

192

That's why I refused a lot of jobs, because it was too much for me. I wasn't going to have it run me crazy. I would just take in the walk-in trade. There were quite a few churches in my neighborhood and I used to do a lot of their work. Coin envelopes and raffle tickets. I made enough money to live off of. I didn't save too much, but I could pay my bills and eat what I wanted. Babe worked as a cook in a restaurant. I also taught myself photography by reading books. There weren't always color films, so I hand-colored my own prints. I had my own darkroom and had it set up in a coal bin.

Our house was noted for being the "gay spot." There weren't very many places in Detroit you could go [to] back in 1937, 1940. We rented out the back 4 rooms of downstairs to a gay fellow. When we had a party, we would open up the whole house. People used to come from everyplace. They'd be all out in the yard, upstairs and downstairs. Sometimes people would bring their own bottle. They would get so drunk, everybody would get to fighting. I'd be looking on because I didn't know how to fight. Next morning, I'd be sweeping up hair from women fighting. And the boys would fight out in the yard. Now, I wasn't a drinker. If I drank anything, I'd put it in the little cap of the bottle. That would be my portion. Put ginger ale or Coca Cola in that, sip on it. But my girlfriend could drink!

Babe and I were two different types of people. She liked to go a lot, gamble and drink, but I didn't take that up at all. I was the stay-at-home type. But we made it pretty well. I learned to accept her faults. A lot of people would ask me, "Why don't you leave her?" That was my home, so I just stayed. I had hobbies of my own like my photography to take up my time, and we had a couple of dogs. Whenever she'd leave the house, she knew the dogs would be taken care of because I'd be there. I liked my home. We had a nice place and a big yard. Babe remodeled the place, you know. She could knock the plaster off the wall, put in a doorway, do all that kind of stuff. But she never wore pants or anything.

JEWELL: Did you ever cross-dress?

ELLIS: The only time I did that was on Halloween night. I'd

193

put on my brother's trousers.

JEWELL: Is your home still standing?

ELLIS: No, the city had it torn down during "Urban Renewal." Babe and I separated then because I wanted to live downtown since I had no car. Babe had a car and wanted to live up near where she worked, so she moved out to Southfield. I had a key to her place and I could come and go as I wanted, but she couldn't have a key to my place. Where I lived, they wouldn't let a resident have 2 keys. I lived at the Wolverine Senior Citizen housing complex for 16 years in downtown Detroit. Then, I moved to my present address, still in downtown Detroit, and I've been here for 3 years.

Babe had a child when she was 17, before she got out of school. Her daughter got mixed up in dope, then broke herself of the dope habit. But she got on a whiskey habit and then she wouldn't eat anything. She became dehydrated and had to be put on a respirator. The daughter had 4 children and they were scattered around at different people's houses. But now they're doing very well for themselves. I never see them, though. Babe died in 1973. Her daughter passed about a month afterwards. Babe's daughter never knew that her mother had died.

Now, is this a story? To me it's nothing. Some people have all their life mixed up. There's so much happening in their life. Not mine. My life is ordinary. Calm. I love to dance, bowl and go to classical music recitals. I have many young friends who treat me wonderfully. They make me feel young! I'm having a lot of fun for a 90-year-old woman!

Mommy Always Knows
by Kimberly "Q" Purnell

My coming out process wasn't as difficult as many would
imagine. My advantage was that my uncle (who passed from
AIDS) on my mother's side was an openly gay man, so he kind
of made the transition easier for me, but here's my story.

I remember from a very young age never wanting to be
intimate with a man. I remember telling my mother that I would
never have sex with a man because it was "NASTY." By the time
I was 18, I had had many, many sexual interludes with various
types of women and still had no physical attraction to men. My
mother encouraged me to at least date so that I couldn't say I
didn't give men a fair chance. I subsequently dated and slept with
many, many men (in addition to still having relationships with
women); I also became a very heavy drinker (I couldn't sleep
with the men unless I was totally "FULL!"). After two years, I
decided I didn't like being with men physically (even though I
knew this before) and decided it was time to tell my family and
friends.

From the time I was about 10 years old, I didn't really know
what a lesbian was. I had read stories about women being
intimate together, but I thought it was OK since it felt so good!
As I got older, I didn't know there were other women like me
with the exception of the ones I was with. Every time I was
intimate with a woman, I always thought people knew it the next
day.

At 20, I was in school and living with my father in Illinois. I
found the book *Loving Someone Gay* and read it. I sent a copy to
my mother in New Jersey. At the same time, my father found a
letter from the woman I was dating at the time, and called me at
work to find out what the hell was going on!

He accused me of being sick, and told me it came from my
mother's side of the family (because of my uncle). He then told
me I had to move out! I was very hurt — I've always been a
"Daddy's Girl" — and moved from his apartment.

After two weeks of not hearing from my mother, she finally
called and we talked. She told me she always knew it when I was

195

growing up, but thought that I would grow out of it. She also asked me to give my father some time to adjust. From that point, I began telling the rest of my family: five sisters, one brother, 17 cousins and multiple aunts, uncles, grandparents, friends and co-workers.

Well, one year later, my father finally came around; he called me. During our talk, he informed me that he wanted me to meet this woman who worked with him. He said, "She's, you know, funny like you!" He told me she drove a truck for one of the companies that delivered to his job. I was not interested, mind you, but understood that was his way of accepting.

Out of all this, I lost two (so-called) friends, but have gained respect from many who don't view me as a lesbian because of what I look like. My activism and community work tend to make people take a reality check and respect me for who and what I am.

Mothers Know
by Shay Youngblood

I was scared mama would look at me and know I was changed
that first time Jesse came home with me. All my years of living
with mama I knew she'd see deeper than skin could cover. I was
scared she would cut her eyes at Jesse and know she was a
lesbian, take one swift look at me and know I was deep in love
with her. After her knowing I could only pray she didn't have a
stroke. But mama hugged Jesse close like she was blood too.

When I was growing up, somewhere I learned early that
women who liked other women were funny, or bull daggers.
They looked, dressed and acted like men and were going against
the nature of women to have babies. I also learned that it was
supposed to be a white woman's disease, but that didn't make
sense to me, because the only lesbian I ever knew when I was
growing up was Tam and she was deep sun browned and I
looked like her shadow.

They used to say Tam was funny. She didn't straighten her
hair, wear dresses or take shit off nobody. I didn't notice nothing
funny about Tam. She wore blue jeans and workshirts everyday
to her job at the mill and sharp tailored pant suits on her days off.
Those days she would brush back her short afro and go out
driving in her white mustang convertible. Mama would push me
behind her as she and Aunt Tullie looked out the screen door
toward Tam's apartment, shaking their heads and talking about
Tam. They used to look down at me telling me to act like a lady
or no man would want me. Remembering back then, I surely
wasn't thinking about no man. As a matter of fact I was thinking
about how much I wanted to be like Tam. She didn't let nobody
tell her what to do and didn't care what folks said about her, even
when they said it to her face.

When I looked in the mirror I didn't look funny, just felt real
different from other girls. In high school I didn't go out with
boys. Mama was proud that I was a good girl, not counting my
thoughts. Mostly I was scared of having a baby I didn't want and
scared of my feelings for other girls. Mama warned me to stay
away from boys because they would ruin me and not get too

197

close to girls because they either wanted your man, to know your business or they wanted to mess with you. "And once you get into that sinful habit with women, no man will want you," she would say. I still didn't want no man.

At the dinner table mama fussed over both me and Jesse, piling our plates high with collard greens, candied yams and corn bread, begging us to eat some dangerously delicious smelling fried pork chops, even though I said we didn't eat meat.

"Jesse will you make certain my other child eats? She ain't got sense god give a cow when it comes to nourishment. She'd eat grass and chew cud if nobody watched her. All she thinks about is books."

Jesse put her eyes on me and smiled when she answered mama. "I'll make sure she eats m'am. My greens aren't as good as yours, but nobody ever died from my cooking." Mama seemed satisfied that she had someone responsible to look after me. Jesse was older than me by more than 10 years and on top of that she had a respectable sprinkle of gray in her hair and mama said a honest look in her eyes. Neither mama or Aunt Tullie seemed to think our friendship or our decision to live together odd. They had gotten used to Jesse coming home with me on weekends and holidays. They asked her about my old habits and led her to agree with their memories.

"Do she still stay up all times of the night? Used to be she'd hide the lamp light by putting a towel under her door. That child be up reading til day break."

"Yes m'am, she still insist on being up reading when other folks be sleeping."

When I was 14 I stayed up late one night looking out my bedroom window, watching the saturday night crowd come and go. Just past midnight I saw Tam drive up in front of the apartments. She parked under the street light so I could see them clearly. Tam got out of the car and walked her left handed strut around to the passenger side to open the door for her girlfriend Mickey. Mickey was so pretty she made my insides feel light. She was a puerto rican girl with deep dimples and dark laughing eyes. It seemed she was always showing those deep dimples and smiling at Tam, and throwing her long shiny dark hair over her bare shoulders. Mickey got out of the car and leaned back against it. She said something in Tam's ear that made them both laugh. It surprised me when Tam took Mickey's hand and said something that made her smile it seemed toward my window. They held hands as they walked to Tam's apartment like it was a everyday thing. In that moment of illumination under bright street lights I began to wonder what it would feel like to hold my best friend, Connie's hand. Tam stopped just outside my window and kissed Mickey on the mouth before they went inside her apartment. After a while Tam's lights went out but I still imagined them kissing in the dark. That led to my wondering what it would be like to kiss Connie on the mouth in the dark and whisper secrets in her ear and make her laugh from loving her with my breath.

The discovery of a woman's mouth on mine came often after that, mostly in my day dreams but sometimes for real. I spent more time with Connie. Mama knew then that something was going on when Connie and I stayed locked up in my room for hours at a time doing our reading exercises. She would let me kiss her and hold her hand while she read out loud. I would watch her lips handle words and feel them pressing against my ear. Mama was somewhere in the house thanking god that I hadn't started courting, boys that is. She never said a word about the affair.

My imagination hadn't prepared me for Jesse. The hot, wet touch of her tongue chasing mine or the way my heart hammered when her hands traced the curves along my face and neck. She saw things in a single cloud that made my eyes seem new when I looked. We saw things in each other that made being together feel as if we were under a spell. After two years the love still felt magic.

Mama knew something happened then. In the air I guess. She called me up the morning after and asked me if I was ever going to settle down since I was almost finished with college.

"If you're talking about marriage mama, forget it, I'm much too independent for that kind of arrangement."

"Annie Lee's daughter wanted to be independent too. She run off to New York wid a woman. It hurt Annie Lee bad. Said she'd rather see the child pregnant out of wedlock than to see her shack up like that with another woman, without shame. It ain't natural,"

Mama said.

It was only my first day being an official newly initiated lesbian and I just wasn't ready to tell mama about Jesse and me so I changed the subject and said a prayer my mama never find out before I tell her.

Jesse said she'd never tell her very christian, very proper mother. When she was 16 her mother burst into her room with tears in her eyes and demanded to know if she was a lesbian. "The way she said lesbian, I knew I'd better say no. But she didn't give me time to answer before she went on about how she had found and read a letter my girlfriend Marie had written to me saying how much she loved me and what we did together. Mama talked about how perverts were sinners and she would have neither in her house. She read to me from the bible and made me swear on it not to see Marie again. Later I realized that she came to me knowing but couldn't face the fact that I was very butch and sexually active."

When dinner was over Aunt Tullie came over and promptly fell into endless conversations with Jesse. When we were leaving Aunt Tullie praised my selection in friends.

"You two take care of each other up there in the city. It's a mighty rough place and friends gotta stick together."

The following spring I had gotten up enough nerve to tell mama about me and Jesse but before I could get a word in she had a piece of news for me. "You know they buried Mr. Harris Sunday before last. Folks was saying he was gay. Must have been cause the church was full of them. Even so, he always was nice to me, then too he paid his church dues more regular than most of the deacons." The words got stuck in my throat and I left them there that time.

Then Aunt Tullie died. I was home for the weekend so I was there to comfort mama. Jesse drove 200 miles to be with me. She brought my black dress, cooked meals for dozens of people she didn't know and locked the door behind the last to leave. Even through her grief mama saw.

"I'm glad that you two have each other. Sometimes I envy youth, but I had 47 years with someone I loved. A woman needs companionship." She smiled, looking at us far off like she was in another time.

After mama had her gall bladder operation Jesse was the one to think of asking mama to come stay with us till she got on her feet again. Finally convinced she wasn't putting us out, she came.

Mama stepped into our living room full of Jesse's plants and my books everywhere and she shook her head in approval.

"You girls got it looking like a home. I like this house, it's full of love. A house with growing things is full of love. It's a fine house daughters," she said looking around the room.

"Both of you already old maids. Guess you two ain't never getting married, are you?" she asked not really expecting an answer.

"No mama I guess not," I said looking over at Jesse as we led her to our bedroom.

No Half Steppin'
by Shilanda Woolridge

Before you can come out to anyone, you have to come out to yourself. Coming out to myself was a slow process that took several years. I think I've always known that I was a lesbian. Deep down in the darkest corner of my subconscious mind, the truth was waiting patiently for me to acknowledge it.

I remember the first time I felt lesbian desire. I was in elementary school, probably third or fourth grade. I was bike-riding in the woods with a playmate of mine named Angela. Later that afternoon, we stopped at a wild strawberry patch to pick some berries. As we walked and talked, I looked at Angela and found myself wondering what it would be like to kiss her. I debated asking her if she would like to kiss and I decided against it for several reasons. A) Well... we were both girls and it would be wrong for us to kiss, of course. B) What if she gets upset and tells all our mutual playmates what happened? Everyone would think I was gross, and no one would want to be my friend anymore. C) Or even worse, she gets upset and tells her parents. Then her parents would contact my parents and all HELL would break loose. In hindsight, I'm glad I didn't ask Angela to kiss because B, C, or both B and C probably would've taken place. However, I never forgot that moment. I guess I should've considered it a foreshadowing of events to come.

Fast forward to my junior year in high school. At the time, I was a very active member in the small black Baptist church that my family attended. I was an usher and choir member, and attended Bible Study on Wednesdays and Sunday School before morning service. Believe it or not, Bible Study was the setting of another lesbian stepping-stone in my life. From time to time, homosexuality was discussed, and I found myself paying close attention to every word spoken during these lessons. Various Bible verses and the story of Sodom and Gomorrah were twisted, stretched, broken, melted and molded into anti-homosexuality dogma to be spoon-fed to the hungry Christian folk.

The fact that homosexuality was a horrible, disgusting sin against God was pounded into my head over and over. "Those people," the pastor declared, "were not born that way. They are just patterning their lives after a bad influence or people they see on TV!" The worshippers nodded their heads and um-hmmed in agreement. I sat there torn between two different schools of thought. I believed that homosexuality was wrong and that gay people were sinners condemned to Hell. Yet, I found myself fascinated with the subject.

I asked mountains of questions during these lessons. I'm surprised that my sudden interest didn't raise a few eyebrows, since I usually sat in silence during Bible Study. These Bible study lessons jump-started my acute interest in gay issues. Anytime a story concerning gay issues popped up in a magazine, newspaper or TV program, I zeroed in on it. I always had an affinity for the eclectic and bizarre, so I legitimized my newfound interest in gay issues by dumping them into that category.

In the May '91 issue of *Essence* magazine, Linda Villarosa published her coming-out article. I read it over and over and over and over. Then for some strange reason, I left the magazine open to Villarosa's article on my dresser. To this day, I still don't have any idea why I did this. Several days later, my mother came into my room as I was preparing to go to bed for the night. She said, "Shilanda ... you do like boys ... don't you?" I was floored. "Uhhhh .... yeah," I replied. I remember making a specific effort to hesitate before answering her because I didn't want my yes to be a concrete yes. "Oh, okay," she sighed, "I was just wondering. I don't want to have to worry 'bout ya now." Then she quietly slipped out of my room and closed the door behind her. After she left, I thought to myself, "What the Hell brought that on?" Then I spotted the open *Essence* magazine on my dresser. I immediately snatched up the magazine and stuffed it in the back of the closet.

In the fall of '92 I started my freshman year at the University of Texas at Austin. Austin is a thriving young college city and my eyes were opened to a new world. There were several gay clubs (99 percent of them for men) located in the downtown area. In addition, there were gay bookstores like Lobo and Liberty Books. One could find gay and lesbian sections in mainstream bookstores. Back in Abilene, Texas (where I'd spent the previous six years of my life), I had no idea that places like these existed.

In these stores, I had my first encounter with lesbian erotica in the pages of *On Our Backs* and *Bad Attitude* magazines. I even ran across an all African-American lesbian erotica publication titled *Black Lace!!!* Whenever I had a few hours to spare, I would go to a bookstore, plunk my booty down in the aisle and read lesbian lore. Never, ever did I consider purchasing anything; I wouldn't be caught dead with lesbo paraphernalia on my person. Besides, I wasn't a lesbian; I was just curious.

In addition to the clubs and bookstores, there were free weekly newsletters and organizations for gay folks. The *Texas Triangle* (a newsletter for Texas gays), and *Fag Rag* (a social 'zine primarily for men) could be found near the front doors of any trendy coffeehouse, bookstore, or eatery in Austin. On the street, I saw flyers advertising the Lesbian Avengers, OutYouth (a center for young queers and those questioning their sexual identity), and gay university student organizations. I was bombarded from all sides with constant reminders of gayness, which made it harder for me to ignore the feelings I had inside.

Several things made it easier to dismiss those feelings: my boyfriends. I met my first boyfriend during the second semester of my freshman year at UT. Dennis was a 6'3" ex-football player who constantly bragged about his athletic and sexual prowess. He was always nagging me about sex, even though I told him more than once that I was celibate. I had very little interest in fucking Dennis. To be quite honest, I had very little interest in Dennis, period.

I met my second boyfriend while visiting my family during the summer of '93. Malik was very sweet and I cared very deeply for him (deep enough to have my heart broken). But I had to face the fact that what we had was nothing more than a summer fling.

Early in my sophomore year, I met my third and final boyfriend. Antonio was a handsome Chicano with the largest Napoleon Complex this side of the Mississippi. He was a funny, talented writer and artist with an abrasive no-bullshit personality. Antonio aspired to be a filmmaker and put Chicanos on the silver screen. We worked together at the university movie theater and quickly became friends.

Once we started seeing each other seriously, I decided I was ready for sex. It took several painful tries on several occasions before Antonio could get it in and I immediately found myself disappointed. On TV and the movies it looked like it felt soooooooooo good. Sometimes it was really good..... sometimes.

Antonio and I had a wonderful relationship; however, my curiosity about lesbianism began to resurface. Even though I detest the club scene, I would look in the *Fag Rag* at the descriptions of the lesbian clubs and wonder what it was like to go. Unfortunately, all the clubs were for those 21 years and up. I still had almost two years before I could get in!

I was still happy with Antonio, but several months later I decided that I was open to trying sex with a woman. I knew that there was no way I could actually settle down in a relationship with a woman, but I still wanted to know what it was like to have a lesbian sexual experience. I must declare that I am a very monogamous person, and I could never, ever cheat on Antonio. Nor would I break up with him on behalf of my metamorphosing sexual identity because we were happy together. Nothing lasts forever, so I decided that I would let our relationship run its course, no matter how long it took.

In the meantime, I was left to satisfy my curiosity through fantasy. One of my favorite fantasies was a ménage à trois with two other beautiful black women with long dreadlocks and voluptuous breasts. Another outlet for my fantasies was reading the personal ads in the *Austin Chronicle* weekly. There was a Women Seeking Women section that I liked to read. Unfortunately, most of the lesbians that advertised were 30-plus years old.

Reading the personals gave me ideas for my fantasies, but it got really old and unfulfilling after a while. So I moved on to the next best thing ... pornos! Every once in a while, I would go to Pleasureland porn shop and fork over the six bucks to watch a lesbian video in one of their private rooms. This activity became quite addictive for me; it was the closest I could get to the real thing without actually doing anything.

Reading lesbian erotica and watching the pornos became a sexually eye-opening experience for me. I had never felt this

206

aroused in my life. When I was with Antonio, I would start out dry and get drier as our encounter progressed. On the other hand, my fantasy activities made me so slick and wet that I could actually feel myself dripping into my panties. Sometimes I would get so hot that the throbbing in between my legs would become painful. I also admitted to myself that I had an obsession with breasts. I loved ample breasts with large nipples.

Even though it was quite clear that I was sexually attracted to women and not men, I still refused to entertain the idea that I might be a lesbian.

Antonio and I were together for about a year and a half. During the last three or four months, we began to drift apart. I was having personal emotional problems due to stress, depression, and burnout from school. My personal problems made a bad situation — our drifting relationship — worse. Antonio tried to be patient, but it didn't take long for him to get fed up with me. He became very disrespectful toward me, and it hurt. It was only a matter of time before one of us bit the bullet and initiated the breakup.

I was out having dinner with friends when I decided to do it. After dinner, my friends and I went to Antonio's apartment; they waited in the parking lot for me while I took care of business. Antonio was very apathetic about the end of our relationship and acted like my personal problems were the main reason for our breakup. He didn't want to hear about being a short disrespectful little self-centered asshole who took all my kindness for granted. The next time he's in between paychecks and down to his last box of mac & cheese with no one to hook him up with groceries or help him out with a few bucks, he'll look into his empty pantry and think of me. Fuck'em! the bastard could stand to lose a few pounds anyway. It was time to move on, so I did.

Now that I was single, I had all the freedom I needed to explore my sexual identity, but I was unsure of what direction to take. I was afraid to go to any of the gay organizations because I was afraid that someone I knew might see me.

One morning, I was in my bed staring at the ceiling, and I said out loud, "Shilanda, you're a lesbian. No bi-curious straight women would spend this much time thinking about women, fantasizing about sex with women, spending hours reading dyke magazines and books, watching dyke pornos, while obsessing over breasts. Who the fuck do you think you're fooling, kid?"

Wow, there it is, I heard the affirmation of my queerness from my own mouth into my own ears. That wasn't hard at all; in fact, it was rather quick and painless. I felt really weird because I had finally acknowledged what I had known all along, and I felt very comfortable with it. In fact, I felt rather good.

Okay, so the affirmation part took all of twenty seconds. Now it was time to seek out other women like myself. I was still not ready to join a gay organization, so I decided to go to a club, even though there's nothing I hate more than a smoky club filled with drunk people that I can't have intelligent conversations with. However, a club would give me the anonymous exposure that I desired. I would turn 21 in two or three months; anyway, maybe the bouncer would give me a break, since I don't drink.

I picked up the latest issue of *Fag Rag* and, much to my surprise, there was a women's dance club that accepted 18 and up; great! The following Friday, my stomach did flip-flops as I put the finishing touches on my makeup and splashed on some perfume before running outside to catch the last bus downtown. This would be my first time going to a gay event of any kind and I was unsure of what to expect. Once I got off the bus there was no turning back.

As I walked to the club, my mind was swimming with questions. Does this mean that I'm sinning against God? Well, I didn't choose to feel the way I do. Have mercy, what would my family think when they find out? My Mom and Dad would be so disappointed. Especially my Mom, she's always talked about throwing me a big wedding when I found my Mr. Right. Would she and Dad be willing to do the same when I find my Ms. Right? Would my friends still be my friends after I tell them? Where can I meet other African-American lesbians like myself?

The thumping techno music and scent of cigarettes jolted me from my thoughts. I had plenty of time to wrestle with those issues later. I took a deep breath and walked in the front door.

notes to momma
by akhaji zakiya

After changing my name, locking my hair, leaving school and boundlessly discovering that I could love women, all within the space of a year... my Caribbean immigrant, middle-class aspirant parents were suffering growing pains. So was I.

This piece is excerpted from a letter written to my mother during our estrangement.

91.04.22

momma, momma, momma,

as i let myself into work, i noticed an envelope that looked amiss in the pile of mail on the desk. when i noticed it was from you, my heart jumped and i immediately began to prepare myself for a blow.

i figured these words were certain to be a follow up to our last phone conversation. the one when i told you i wanted to move back home.

the last couple of weeks have been so draining, so emotionally unbalanced... i am still stinging from your abrupt, disdainful rejection of me. i eyed your letter and prepared for what i was certain would be a "don't you bring your lesbian self back around *here*" tone.

when i was finally ready to open it, i unfolded the single page and quickly directed my eyes to the very last words. i figured the way you ended might be indicative of what you had to say. i saw "love you as always, your beloved Mother" and was somewhat relieved.

since my spontaneous move to boston four months ago, we had
not shared a positive word between us. yet in this note you called
me your "dearest daughter." even tho i'm your only daughter, i
smiled. it is a good feeling to know your mother loves you,
something i am learning not to take as unconditional.

"clean up your act," these words began your second line. you've
said this to me before. on the phone i asked you what it meant, as
in, what would i have to do to make my act clean. you hesitated.
here in your letter you responded with "do something with your
hair, straighten up your life, go back to school."

you did not mention my sexuality (unless that was covered in
"straighten up your life"). but i know it doesn't please you and
you would change it if you could.

you do, however, constantly tell me to stop hanging out with
"those people," and you did not seem impressed that i might get
work on a black lesbian film project this summer.

let me start with my hair. i don't know what more to say to you
on this. cutting my hair is a notion so far removed from my
reality. it is locked into a natural, unprocessed state. a powerful/
spiritual extension of me that makes me feel strong and capable,
i can't even bring myself to trim the pointy ends, far less cut off a
whole lock. this has been a process. as i've grown more knowl-
edgeable, more confident, more understanding of myself, they
too have grown.

you're probably thinking, "now she mussi gone mad, talkin 'bout
she hair so." yet i'm trying to put into words for you, and perhaps
for me, the significance of this stuff on my head. for me, it's not a
trend, it's not fashion. i've desired dreading it from before it was
this popular. but i was afraid. i liked braids because they felt real
and the look was kinda natural (even tho it was plastic hair out of

210

a plastic bag). plus, i didn't have to fuss in the morning.

but these locks are my own hair. my beautiful, afrikan/bajan/
canadian coarse hair. to wash it, to go thru it twisting stray naps
into place, to rub oil on my scalp and on each thick black cord of
me is wonderful, even peaceful and soothing. changing it is not
an option i am interested in exploring anytime soon.

i must admit, there have been times when i've been frustrated
with this head of mine. times when i wake up, happen to look in
the mirror and don't like how short they are, how they stick up,
how the ends look pitiful and how they won't stay where i want
regardless of how i arrange them. and of course i get pissed off
when people, especially blackfolks, look at me funny, hold their
purse tighter or mumble "whoopi goldberg" when i walk by. yes,
i do get frustrated. but i am realizing that *everything,* my hair
included, is a process.

i am going back to school. please know that. but when i return i
want to know why i'm there, i want to enjoy my program or at
least feel motivated to do the work. i need to be in an atmosphere
and headspace where i am learning all sorts of things and connecting their significance to the rest of my life. i want my
education to have meaning and purpose. i don't think that is an
unrealistic expectation.

i started university with motivation and interest, but they faded. i
was unhappy and isolated as one of few black women in first and
second year science courses. busying myself with projects and
people, cutting classes and despising the confines of academe did
not prevent me from wondering why the hell i was there. my
marks were in the toilet. yet they were indicative of how unful-
filled i was rather than a measure of what i'm capable of. perhaps
this doesn't make sense to you. the way you see it i had nothing
to worry about except going to school and "doing well." i wish
that was all.

211

ever since i can remember i've been getting myself together, mom. sometimes it has been easy, and sometimes i pretend i am more confident and stable than i actually am. i am continually sorting things out and working on myself. not 'cuz i think i am a bad person or in need of more self/reflection than others, but 'cuz i know (now) that it is a necessary, healthy aspect of existence. i'm still learning.

it is hard to hear your criticisms of me mom. it is hard to know that you are hurt by my living as i need to live, by my figuring out my own path. my relationship with you is too valuable, too integral to my existence. despite the pain tho, i will only be who i am.

i'll stop now. this is the second time i've written you with the intent of just jotting down a note...

> give my love to the rest,
> your dearest daughter.

Pure
by Tonia Bryan

DEDICATED TO ALL THOSE DIASPORIC DYKES, WICCA
WIMMIN, SODOMITE SISTAS, SUBURBAN SHE-HE'S
AND AFRO-CANADIAN QUEERS WHO CAN'T POSSIBLY
BEGIN TO DESCRIBE WHAT A BLACK LESBIAN LOOKS
LIKE, FEELS LIKE, WALKS LIKE, SOUNDS LIKE OR
TASTES LIKE AND DON'T WANT TO. CUZ SHE IS MUCH.
AS FOR ALL OF YOU WHO NEED TO TELL HER WHO
SHE IS, WHERE SHE'S GOIN' AND HOW SHE'S GONNA
GET THERE ... PISS OFF!

Written in fear. Wondering if I too will be *cast out* or ostracized
because I dare to think for myself, if I speak the *wrong* words or
entertain thoughts that deviate from the supposed *normalcy* of
the collective mentality. What does it mean when the lives and
communities we build to safeguard ourselves from oppression
become almost as unsafe and censoring as the outside world?
When truth-telling and exploration are perceived as a threat?
What does it say for the future of feminism when often it is not
the strength of a woman's convictions but her ability to *fit in*,
that defines real commitment to THE CAUSE?

I

IN THA LIFE, IN THA CLOSET

an acquaintance show us an extremely secret supply of porn
mags she's been hoarding for years. no one knows about it. she
consumes the pictures of silicone-augmented breasts, clipped
pubic hairs and spread vaginal lips like fresh, hot, stolen cookies
— in secret, one by one savouring each moment, licking her
fingers in between.

another lesbian confides in me that she's thinking of locksing her

213

hair. she says the sistas she's *attracted* to don't take her advances seriously, don't really pay her any mind with just an afro on her head.

WILL SOME LOCKS MAKE IT MO BETTA?

I see a beautiful fag/boy at the bar. for months i cruise him wanting to touch him, hold him, maybe fuck him. can't find the courage to walk up to him though. the other wimmin will see. they'll *know* i'm not a *REAL* lezzy.

WE see a *FINE* black woman walk into the bar with a white gyal on her arm. no one moves to greet her. someone says "what a waste." i want to ask her name but i *don't* want to deal with her lover's white supremacy. maybe she'll be like the other white wimmin in the bar wanting to grab and paw some dancing black flesh. because of the company our sista's keepin' no one moves to greet her/embrace her/welcome her/love her. what a damn waste.

SHE goes to women's dances often. HIPS SWINGIN', THIGHS RUBBIN', WAIST WINEIN. SHE'S POSIN' AND POSTURIN' TO THE BEAT OF THE MUSIC, WORKING UP A FUNK LIKE YOU WOULD NOT BEEELIEVE! the other black dykes look her up and down. they often say her skirts are too short, her dresses are too tight, her tops are too transparent, her heels too high. FOR WHO?

Political Dyke Chorus: *COVER UP! COVER UP! WE SAID COVER YOURSELF UP! U OUGHT TO BE ASHAMED. ALL THAT EXPOSED FLESH. WHAT WILL THEY THINK? THE WHITE SUPREMACISTS, THE WOMAN-HATERS OF THIS WORLD. FINDING YOU IN THIS STATE? OVER-SEXED, BRAINLESS, AVAILABLE, FOR SALE. CHILE NOBODY IS GOIN' TO TAKE YOU SERIOUSLY DRESSED LIKE THAT. WHAT SORT OF FEMINIST (CAN SUBSTITUTE WOMANIST)*

214

ARE YOU ANYWAY?

SHE can't help but think they would prefer to see her *wearin'*
some sort of uniform. maybe a tam in ital colours on her head, a
t-shirt with a slogan — something from iwd, take back the night
or pride day will do — on the front, a pair of loose-fitting blue
jeans and on her feet a pair of large boots or birkenstocks with
workmen's socks. is there a wimmin's department store chain or
a feminist factory outlet where she could get tha look, buy tha
look, achieve that look?

WOULD THAT MAKE IT MO BETTA?

THEY are four black dykes up late on community radio. finally
allowed to take over the air waves they're spinnin' tunes and
talkin' about livin' in the life. afterwards one of them remarks
that she would really like to see the show concentrate on more
feminist oriented music. like joan armatrading. does *HER*
feminism have room for patra's feminist thighs? india's feminist
house? chaka's feminist come-back? mary j's feminist booty?
patti's feminist bi-curiousity? rupaul's feminist falsies? adeva's
feminist attitude? tlc's feminist condoms? mc lyte's feminist
make-over? swv's feminist nails? anita's feminist rapture?
donna's feminist hot love? diana's feminist weave? *WHOSE*
feminism is she talkin' 'bout anyhow? all i know is sometimes
when i get tired of deconstructing, decolonizing, theorizing,
strategizing and empowering, my girls bring me back from the
edge. renew me with their words. stroke me with their soul. give
me the strength to go on.

a SISTA called me one afternoon to ask about an image she saw
on a flyer. let me tell u ... it was a truly bizarre conversation. she
was concerned cuz the picture was too ... well ... sexual. that a
man would see it and associate it with black dykes. TELL me
somethin' I don't know. i feel that as a Black dyke there is
pressure put on me to be a super-proper feminist caretaker with

all the answers. never making a mistake. never acting on im-
pulse. always putting the beliefs of the whole before my own. a
sort of moral majority lesbian who shares the mistaken belief
that frank talk about sex/ fuckin'/ porkin'/ doin' the do/ knockin'
the boots is the cultural domain of a few confused, male-identi-
fied white lesbians. truly political african dykes don't talk 'bout
eatin' pussy/ fistin'/ fingerin'/ fuckin' boys — gay or straight/
takin' it in the ass/ golden showers/ scat/ restraints/ play parties
and all that. we're too busy attending collective meetings and
savin' the world. still playin' mammy. shit!

yeah i know black wimmin have been eroticized by most of the
known world because of racism, white supremacy, misogyny and
the patriarchy. yeah i know that we are often cast as hookers/
sexual deviants/ nymphomaniacs/ castrating voodoo queens/
over-sexed/ brainless/ available/ for sale. now tell me somethin' i
don't know. to *hell* with take back the night! what good is it if i
can't experience all of myself? i wanna take *BACK* my SEX/
uality — putting it back where it belongs: in my heart, in my
gaze, in my words, at the tips of my nipples, in the hollow of my
neck, in the pulse of my clit and deep, deep inside of my
poonani. in a society where black people's/ wimmin's/ lesbian
sexuality has been perverted, subverted, commercialized and fed
back to us, we need to find ways to *act* not *react* to other
people's twisted assumptions. we need to spend less time plot-
ting counter-moves, constantly responding to outside pressures,
assumptions and misconceptions. we need to reclaim, recolonize
all the lands and people inside uh we. we need to take the *time* to
explore every nook and cranny of *ourselves* without shame or
fear.

feelings of total frustration. i'm tired of being tied in knots. tired
of doing as i'm told. there is a screaming mad banshii inside of
me that wants to talk back, to cuss out feminism's Black/
'coloured' power brokers, academia and media elite for aiming
their oppressed, suppressed, self-censored brand of politics at
this Black ass. I wanna say: "I did *NOT* come out so I could go
into a deeper closet with *YOU!*"

216

II

AFRICAN LESBIAN IDENTITY GAMES

NO RIGHT OR WRONG ANSWERS HERE. RESPOND AS
YOUR HEART BIDS. LEAVE THAT UNIFORM AT THE
DOOR. STRIP TO THE BONE. NAKED AS THE DAY YOUR
MOMMA PUSHED YOU FORTH.

SHALL WE BEGIN? WHAT DOES SHE SMELL LIKE?
egyptian musk, raw sweat, ck-1 or cunt juice?

WHAT ARE HER CLOTHES LIKE? is she wearin' a kente
cloth wrap? a guatemalan print jumper? a sequined ball gown? or
black leather chaps?

IS SHE READING — the everywoman's almanac? this bridge
called my back? on our backs? or black lace? when she fucks
herself?

DOES HER IDEAL WOMAN RESEMBLE alice walker? sade?
a gay man? or k.d. lang?

WHEN ASKED DOES SHE — call herself black first, dyke
second? the other way around? of colour? or does she when
pressed, express her dislike for labels of any kind?

AND HOW HAS SHE SOLVED THE EVER-PRESENT
NAPPY HAIR SITUATION? is her only choice dreadlocked
radicality? has she opted for a slick ZHANE sensibility? are wigs
more her thang? or is a sharp razor her styling tool of choice?

217

WOULD SHE PREFER — an astronomically priced one bedroom off of church? an unregistered basement dwelling in
scarberia? a pad over a trendy queen street store? or a not too
romantic room in the family home?

QUICK! SHE'S RUN OUT! DOES SHE SEND YOU TO THE
CORNER STORE FOR — a box of unbleached environmen-
tally-safe tampons? a dime bag? or a new supply of SWV press-
on nails?

ANSWER CAREFULLY. YOU WILL BE JUDGED, GRADED
AND *ALWAYS* FOUND WANTING.

III

SAMENESS, COLLECTIVITY, COMMON CULTURE AND OTHER FEMINIST MYTHS

please do tell me i need instruction is there a class i can take, a
correspondence course i can send away for to become a pure
one? a super one? a proper one? you know like ...
DYKEASPORIC WIMMIN 1001? OR AFRICAN LESBIAN
TONGUES UNTIED FOR BEGINNERS?

the instructors would teach me proper black lesbian feminist
etiquette. the lesbian arts and media censorship department
would tell me what pictures to draw, what photos to love.
PRAISE BE TO THE GODDESS! I've been feeling sorta lost
since i left kindergarten. They would decide *for* me what work is
political and what creations stand against the cause.
WOULDN'T WANT TO OFFEND, DISPLEASE, CHAL-
LENGE, STIMULATE OR BROADEN THE *SCOPE* OF THE
CAUSE.

Been feeling rather lost and in need of direction since i left

218

kindergarten. So tell me... should my 2-d wimmin always be clad in turtle necks, loose fitting ethnic print pants and home-made knit socks?

GODDESS SAVE ME! FROM PLUNGING NECKLINES, BIKINI TOPS, POUM-POUM PRINTERS, BATTY RIDERS, CROTCHLESS PANTIES, DILDOS, EXPOSED BELLY BUTTONS, FROM HICKEYS, ERECT NIPPLES, ROCK HARD CLITS AND FROM OBSCENITIES SCREAMED WHILE CUMMING. THESE CAN ONLY HINDER BLACK DYKES FIGHT AND EXPOSE US TO THE LASCIVIOUS GAZE OF THE WHITE, MALE-DOMINATED RIGHT.

IV

THE TRUTH ACCORDING TUH ME

THE AFRICAN LESBIAN — RADIANCE PERSONIFIED IN ALL HER DIVERSITY. A MODEL OF LIFE-SAVING CON-TRADICTION. A MIND BOGGLING EXAMPLE OF UNPREDICTABILITY AND ANARCHY. DEFINITELY NOT AN ENDANGERED SPECIES as contrary to popular belief she comes in all different shapes, sizes, shades, styles, beliefs, politics and hairdos. and does she *EVER* come.

Getting off to the sounds of drag queens, disco queens, folksy utopian dreams, hip-hop scenes and alternative screams. Getting off at the taste of tofu, ground provisions, soya milk, chittlin's, baby back pork ribs, oxtail, kraft dinner and pennies-a-glass-white sugar-laden koolaid. Getting off at the thought of last year's iwd, last week's melrose place, last night's pussy on her face and a close below the knee cap shave. Getting off at the sight of older, stronger, wiser wimmin cussin' and carryin' on *BAD*. at the sight of faggots in lust. at the sight of a stone butch with cock in hand. at the sight of porn mag centerfolds — grown wimmin with breasts, thighs, bellies and BACK! SHE GETS

219

OFF! Gettin' down so you can't pin her down or box her in. controlling her actions. defining her dreams. Thumbing her nose at all y'all who need her to do as she's told not as she *feels*.

DEDICATED TO POMO AFRO HOMOS **EVERYWHERE!*** REFUSING TO TOE THE PARTY LINE — ONE — MORE — INCH. Refusing to *OBEY*. Obediently cutting, pasting, shrinking identities to suit someone else's agenda, to suit someone else's politics and quieten someone else's fears.

DEFINITELY *NOT* PURE ONES. NEVER *CLAIMED* TO BE SUPER ONES. Defying description. Expanding our minds beyond the limits of imposed definition.

V

MAKIN' WAY, MAKIN' SENSE

so sick and tired of the socio/historico/politico/diasporical moral majority SHIT! so tired of the big sista dictatorship, masqueradin' as benevolent matriarchal concern. tired of deconstructin', decolonizin', theorizin', respondin', reactin' and strategizin'. tired of never feelin' safe enough to speak my mind, usin' the words i know best. tired of somebody else always knowin' what is best for me. tired of being tied in nice, neat feminist knots. tired of being chastised, threatened and led like a dog on a leash. i am just plain sick and tired of the political dyke

---

* POMO AFRO HOMOS are a Black Gay Male performance group from the States. They brought their original work, *Fierce Love*, to Toronto in the spring of 1994. A combination of song, dance and theater, their work examines they myth and reality of Diasporic African Gay men in the US with much caustic wit, irreverence, unflinching honesty, self-love and historical under-standing.

220

games!

able to speak and write freely at last. i have nothing to lose, whole worlds of self-respect to gain. i must still reckon with my own fear of speaking the unspeakable and with community taboos around the airing of dirty laundry. yet i must persevere. the sight of my own words helps me find a place in the real world away from empty, lifeless theory. away from a feminism based on the notion that the personal is political which nonetheless leaves little room for those of us whose personal lives and personal thoughts regularly cross all sorts of political lines and ideological boundaries. away from dis/eased community dynamics where well-mannered, middle-class silence and complacence are rewarded with job security and access to information. where questioning, resistance and perception are often met with anger, underemployment and isolation. in such a climate my ability to speak up and to document my thoughts grounds me, reminds me of who i am, that i exist. allows me the space to acknowledge all that i am/we are.

WE/Black/Diasporic/African/West Indian/immigrant lesbians are many. We are not the same. I am a dark skinned sista with a difference. No right or wrong answers here. Responding as my heart bids. As my individuality requires. Leavin' the uniforms and labels at the door. Stripped to the bone. Naked as the day my momma pushed me forth. **Strivin' to be real.** Really real. really *MY*/self.

Q & A
by Karen Thompson

So you want to know what it means to be a dyke

after i woke up i strangled a little in my trying not to think about
IT and HER and then i washed my body and then i washed the
glasses and then the plates and finally the pyrex dish and when i
was all done with that i washed the floor on my hands and knees.
By the time i reached the door my whole body felt like a fraction
of the grandmothers who had come before mrs johnson sho nuff
you kitchen is clean as can be oh beulah what would we do
without you you're the bestist maid a family ever had! i uncurled
my spine and ignored the throbbing and thought how lucky i was
that all i had to be worried about today was love and when i
stood up i felt better.

we never have to freak because of forgotten pills/creams/placed
diaphragm/request to give half of the money for the abortion/
IUD/norplant/cancer causing piece of hell made by some undis-
turbed testicle sporting doctor in a white coat and so the passion
continues completely without the influence of the male gender
we think about the heaving seething singing tight careening
feelings without stopping or thinking "what if he puts his hand
on the rolls of fat that cover my belly and screams in horror of
my body leaving me here alone?" we think about our bedrooms
as our own we want you to think about looking in a mirror cause
that's it but different

MARLON RIGGS WAS A FAGGOT African-american
Jamaican-american don't want you you have no place in my
revolution or god's see this war belongs to the straight and those
of you who can't enter our heaven stop shaking the earth
AUDRE LORDE WAS QUEER hell is made up of homosexuals who love children as they should be loved and homosexuals
who survived death camps in shame or died while still alive
homosexuals who sang the blues on stage and to positive needles
homosexuals who painted the sistene and the sky and hell is full
of homosexual daughters mothers and your ancestors friends and
progeny **JAMES BALDWIN WAS A FAIRY** but your brown
don't give you no passport and neither does the kink in your hair
isms only happen to the tinted and that pink triangle on your
chest don't do jack but tell me to get the fuck away from you
cause i never want to be without my stereotypes **LINDA
VILLAROSA IS A DYKE.**

pressed snatch to snatch and feeling large and small and drinking
without danger and loving without anger the beat sounds away in
your skin and the smell of beads of sweat between the fine hairs
on the space above her lipsticked lip draws you and the music
loud and chaotic in your ears but no more chaotic than the soul
that is dancing hard trying to escape out to join hers but seems to
be stuck somewhere in the ribs between your teeth and her left
breast

i am a queen a fairy a dyke a manroyal a sodomite eve a faggot a
queer a punk a bulldagger butch femme bent as my natural hair
and gay as a lily and anything that moves hell i'm so fine i should
throw a party for myself and have god foot the bill

so what does it mean to be a dyke?

none of your goddam nosy ass breeder business

damn

Spice
by Mattie Richardson

By the time I figured out what was really going on, I had already given myself over to her. I handed myself over to a white girl who had never seen me at all. I mean, she didn't have any trouble visually seeing me, she just couldn't bring herself to visualize my existence.

"How does it feel being like you are?" I asked Jen Cutter, who at the time was the big dyke on campus. She could tell I didn't know any better than to say something like that. Jen just laughed, leaned over to me and whispered, "I could always show you."

I was simultaneously scared out of my mind and desperately in love. Sporting her recently shorn dykely haircut and newly acquired black leather motorcycle jacket, she was the essence of lesbian for me; in fact, Jen was the first out lesbian I ever met. This was my first year in college and I had discovered, to my surprise, that I was attracted to women. I decided not to tell anyone until I could find one to ask what it is lesbians do, anyway.

Jen taught me about everything that lesbians did. From her I was introduced to the world of dyke culture and history. She gave me a stack of the required reading to become a full-fledged lesbian. Fortunately, this reading included a few Black lesbians like myself. The college I went to was virtually all-white in a predominantly white New England town. If there were other Black people who were queer, I didn't know about them growing up and they were not visible on campus.

Jen introduced me to other out white lesbians on campus, all six of them. Along with Jen, they formed a small cadre of radical activist lesbians. Their goal was to push a few existing progressive campus organizations further left. I joined their ranks with Jen. I borrowed a friend's leather jacket, smoked Camels, and learned how to discuss Foucault and Fanon in diners for hours. I felt like I was with people who had a better grip on politics and philosophy than anyone I had ever encountered. I felt that not only was I among friends, but real allies.

I thought Jen knew almost everything. She had traveled

extensively and her parents worked for a moderate-to-liberal major magazine. Their assignments took them all over the world and sometimes Jen would get to go with them. As a result, she had an impressive collection of craftwork from India, Brazil, Senegal ..., anywhere her parents went without her they brought back a present. They also brought her whatever recipes they could cajole from the local people. Jen and I spent the weekends in her room making love, talking and creating dishes from around the world. I told her everything about my life. I trusted her completely.

We broke up one wintery Sunday afternoon after we had spent the weekend hanging out in her room. It was cold outside, but sunny so that the room was filled with a pale, blanching light. It made all of her souvenirs look odd and dull. She picked up her camera and started snapping pictures of me in my pajamas in various silly poses. We were both laughing and having fun. After taking the pictures for a while, she laughed out loud to herself. It wasn't until I pressed her for the joke that she told me. It had suddenly occurred to her that I matched the room. I gave it extra flavor. I was the spice.

that beat
by sharon bridgforth

it was the atmosphere   the sound of
dreams spinning jazz   playing
bass   player slouched   into
nodd   and the beat.   it was the
smell of wishful thinking   and cleavage
glasses clinking   nipples rippling
and heels. it was the sight of
a girls bar/smokey   and fullapussy
that drew me and made me feel at home ....

i saw her my first night
out.
she was rich,
deep brown rich/thick lashed
full haired/swinging ass rich
tits
rich
black
rich
diva stalking
rich.
and when she said hello
i melted.

          look baby
          i like
          sapphires and lace

indigo leather and champagne,
money on my dresser,
satin under my ass
and that girl cooking
in the back room/that
candy/that pipe
boiling
hot
i like
wy'mn/as many
as can handle
me   soft/round/tall/short
women/riding in the dark and
that beat/that beat/that
beat/i am
expensive.
baby can you afford me?

my room was lonely.
not big enough
to move in
just lonely
and small.
thats what i thought as
we kissed for the first time/how
small and lonely
the feel of my face pressed
against the window/against
the rain looking out
seeing nothing.

just lonely.
i thought how nice it would be
to hear another heart
beat.
any
body's.

                                          baby,
                                          if you can keep
                                          me the way i
like
                                          to be kept
                                          i will give you
my
                                          time, my
tongue, my
                                          voice like
                                          thunder/if
                                          you let me i
will
                                          control you
                                          so you
                                          never
                                          have to be
                                          responsible
                                          for your own
                                          happiness
                                          again.
                                          baby can you
afford me?

i stayed
for awhile
under her weight/happy
for the pressure/the
reminder
i was alive,
but that bitch got heavy.

                    i am
                    cream
                    come
                    out
                    smooth/easy.
                    say you want yours black?
                    baby thats me
                    straight-up
                    night sky
                    moving in your direction
                    bringing whatever
                    you like/carrying it
                    well.
                    i will become a
                    pre-occupation/a
                    sho-nuff rock
                    yo nerve
                    addiction.
                    one nasty black
                    habit.
                    baby can you afford me?

i heard it
once too often/got
tired of

                 buy me baby
                      buy me
                           baby
                                you have to

umph

                   buy me.

i had visions
of rage boiling over/slamming
continuous/syncopated
beats
out
all over
swinging
       naw

you will have to leave now
                 got to get a gig
               get a gig
                    get a gig
                      got
                         to
                            get a
                               new gig.
baby.

The Journey
by Ekua Omosupe

As a child
I began this journey
to myself
looking for safe harbors
full moons
and a bosom
on which to rest my head

At twelve
I met Annie
a girl
who was also searching
for warmth   comfort   and arms
to hold her tight
we wrestled belly to belly
on the living room sofa
after Momma fell asleep
our eager kisses
and hungry fingers
tasted warm secrets
and sealed a pact between us
girl friends
who swore not to tell
what we found between each other
in the middle of that hot
North Carolina summer

We kissed and licked each others'
disappointments and hurts
to an innocent ecstasy
until
prying eyes and an uninvited guest
discovered us naked
without excuse
in the middle of the afternoon

on my mother's day bed
we were scared   angry   mute
in the face of accusation and whispers
"funny   funny"
"you girls are not normal"
"normal"
"normal"
we ran from ourselves
and from each other
enemies
who avoided each other's gazes
forgot our pact of sisterhood
and girlfriends
rumors spread
and we used them like stones
against each other
the distance between us grew into a gulf
and we each set sail
in different directions
looking for safe harbors
full moons
a bosom to rest our heads

At twelve
we did not know
that there were others like us
women
who kissed   held hands   made love
to each other in secret
our risk was theirs also

I do not know where
this first lover of mine
has gone to
I do not know what harbors she found
I hope she is safe
in woman arms
and is lulled to sleep with deep heart kisses

I too have traveled far
and battle against my own fears
of being caught naked
again
by prying eyes
and shamed by some one else's fears
on this journey
to myself
at every chance
I anchor at harbors
that feel safe
where
women stand guard
on the shore
and lull me to rest

I learn that safety is where we
make it
and I too
stand guard
at the shores
of women's lives
protecting
nurturing
loving
lulling them to rest

The Making of an Orphan: the death of a daughter's place in the family

a healing in progress

by sherece taffe

"When it looked like the sun... she wasn't gonna shine no more, the goddess put a rainbow in the sky." *Maya Angelou (more or less)*

this piece started — in my head — 3rd june 1995, the day of my daughter's fifth birthday party, when the three "family" members that showed up spent the entire time in another room away from the festivities looking and acting like doom and gloom. my sister had my daughter getting things for her so that she wouldn't have to enter the kitchen or the backyard where the party was in full swing. my cousin sat with his jacket on the entire time. and my mother let it slip that i had missed — because i wasn't invited — my sister's college graduation the night before. that's when i realized that not only were they not interested in being a part of my life, but apparently i was not invited to be a part of their life either.

ONE

ong after she stopped talking to me, i continued to daydream about deep respectful intimate conversations between the two of us, mother & daughter, adults sharing life stories... even when she dialed my number and refused the pretext of small talk, i imagined us engaged in intensely spiritual and powerful discussions... i pretended to talk to her about the women in my life, about my hopes and plans and dreams for the future. as many times as reality slapped, shook and yes, punctured my fantasies, i held on to hope... held on to the notion that she would come around; that she would one day reach out to my existence and *inquire about/become curious/show interest in* ME!

237

TWO

my mother would prefer for me not to exist. or at least return to the lie of my pre-coming out self. she doesn't even look at me any more when she sees me. it made me feel invisible for a long time; and for a while i felt guilty for... for her not wanting to have anything to do with me; for the look of disappointment i felt her give every time she refused to acknowledge me; for being relieved to get her machine if i had to pass on any information to her. growing up catholic has made it all too easy for me to claim guilt and agonize over my imagined sins.

THREE

i have begun to have nightmares. i imagine that i'm caught in the middle of a busy highway with a car coming directly at me while i keep screaming "mommy! mommy!" but there is no one there but me and the car is getting closer and just before it hits me i see the driver's face but she seems not to see or hear me and it's my mother. once hit, i scream an endless sorrowful scream that ends in my throat but she never looks back. & i wake up in a sweat, shaking, screaming.

FOUR

i feel alone... as if i have no family. and although i've wished to not be a part of my family at times, this feels wrong; feels like there is no connection. feels like i'm suspended in a time, place, space without time. feels like i don't exist anymore. the more i try not to think of family, the more isolated i become and the more fragile i feel. makes me do reckless things. makes me drink & fuck & dream & talk with abandon. makes me want to hurt myself in the hopes that i'll finally be able to feel something. makes me reach for knives to slash the fear. makes me burn myself to extinguish the flames of regret. makes me almost forget that only family could quench my thirst for pain.

i just picked up a book called <u>grandmothers</u>. though i haven't read it yet, i'm reminded of the absence of a grandmother in my life. there doesn't seem to be a way for me to mend the fences long ago torn down. i don't remember how the rift became so great. all i know is that it has been years since i've actually thought of getting in contact with them; years since i've grieved for them; years since i've longed for them; years since i've cried for them — the grandmothers. now i cry for hours. how can i know me if i don't know them?

FIVE

today i wake with longing. longing for a home. longing for an idea of home. longing for that place that is safe. that place where i can go when i'm rejected in all those other places. that place that *does/has/will* not ever exist for me. today i wake with longing and realize i don't know what i long for. do i yearn for a mother, a family? do i ache to belong? does the fear of my aloneness and my exile cause me to look back with longing at a bond long ago washed away by my own tears? today i wake with longing but unable to grasp the threads of my search, i go back to sleep and dream of death.

SIX

i suppose that my mother pushed me forth with all the dreams within her. i suppose the first moment mother peered into the face of the progeny, she saw the image of herself. the perfection that she lacked. the person she *could/would/should* have been. the image of herself re/created. i suppose she planned the life she should have led for this new mini version of herself. i suppose she dreamed wonderful dreams about the flawless life her clone would have and i suppose all the effort these dreams took to create must have made mother guide, more than a little

239

gently, the progeny down the chosen path only to be devastated when the progeny strayed. in other words; after everything she did for me i still went and did exactly what i wanted with no regard for her happiness.

1t occurs to me that i invent her truth. i can't really know what she felt as she pushed me forth. i have never gathered cour age to ask. i still find it hard to approach my mother; to engage her in conversation; to let go of the resentment i feel toward her. to allow myself to be angry. angry at the distance between us. angry at the dislike in her eyes. angry about her denial of my feelings. though she could not have realistically been expected to read my mind, know what i lacked and provide it, i can not seem to let go of the idea that she should have known; that somehow she should have rescued me; that had she cared, she would have known how to love me the way i NEEDed to be loved. she would have known how to protect me when i NEEDed protecting.

SEVEN

1am a lesbian. i have not actually spoken those words to my "family." i've written poems. i've written letters. i've spoken *about* loving women. i've failed to speak the words that are my life. i've failed to make it real. really real. how can i expect them — expect her — to come to terms with my being a dyke if i can't even say the words to her. face to face. after reading my letter and my coming out poems, my mother informed me that she had nothing to say to me but that when she does find the words she hoped that i would listen. since then she has asked to speak with me once. i think that i have needed to come to terms with my own self-definition before i could begin to bridge the gap that is between us. that being said, i realize that our rift is not due to my coming out, but rather to my growing up.

240

h ow does a mother let go of the control she has over the life of her child. once she has provided all she can. once she has planted the seeds of independence in her child, how can she be gracious in letting go when her heart tells her the child still needs her protection. the trouble with my mother stems from the trouble with me. how could i communicate with her when i *didn't know/wouldn't admit* who i was? the more i retreated, the more she advanced until i began to blame her for my unhappiness, my loneliness. she couldn't understand the reasons for my withdrawal, i couldn't understand the reasons for her prying, so the lines were drawn. she became my opponent in a battle neither could win.

EIGHT

W hen i was younger i spent a lot of time trying to please my mother. i got good grades, i was polite, i tried to stay out of "trouble." then i began to resent her for the restrictions that i imagined she put on me. this caused me to try and distance myself from her. the easiest way to do this was to do the things that i knew she wouldn't approve of. i drank and cussed, lied and stole. i tried to be other than myself. this is all tied up with what i imagined to be the "rules of conduct" that i was made to live by. i wrote poems about the loss of our relationship. some i gave to her others i kept to myself. i remember one of the first poems i wrote, when i was twelve, about the loss of my mother who was not lost at all. at least not in the literal sense of the word.

to a MOTHER

i remember when you used to smile

Every

time you saw me coming and i would feel

Loved

just because you are there to make my
Day.
i recall you coming to me with
Warmth
in your voice that made my heart and mind
Sing
whenever you threw those caring words at
Me.
i believe you used to
Laugh
with me and cry when i shed
Tears
of anger and pain instead of now turning
Away.
i suppose you haven't the
Time
to make me feel really good about myself when
You
feel such anguish in your life of chaotic
Energy.
i hope with the core of my
Being
that someday again you will be able to say you're
Glad
i'm here and you didn't make a very regrettable
Mistake
from a DAUGHTER

somewhere along the line we became adversaries. and things
have deteriorated from there.

242

NINE

i thought the birth of my daughter would bring us closer together — even though the *news* of my pregnancy had the opposite effect. surely she would realize that the silent cold war between us could no longer continue. for a short time there was a truce but then things got bleak once again. i think my mother saw my child as the opportunity to create the life that she had failed to create through me. she began — in numerous subtle and not so subtle ways — to tell me that i was not capable of raising a child. thus the commencement of the second silent cold war.

TEN

for four years after my daughter was born i wanted to come out to my mother. for four years i lied to her each time she asked me about the *man* in my life. that's not to say there weren't men in my life. like i said, i lied and this included masquerading as heterosexual. this included keeping silent when my cousin came out and was ostracized by the "family." this included hiding myself from everyone for fear that i would be "discovered" and thrown out of the closet. this included deceiving myself into believing that i loved only *one* woman not all women. let's just say i was in denial and miserable. in march of 1994, my lover of twelve & a half years left me for the last time and that event is one of the main reasons for my coming out. i finally realized that i could no longer hide from myself and came out of the closet of my mind.

ELEVEN

i suppose the idea that she won't get to plan my wedding, that i won't be bringing home *mr. right* or *mr. he'll do* for that matter, has my mother reeling. of course i can only suppose these things because she and i don't really speak. she calls to speak to my daughter. she calls to ask me to do things. she calls to arrange time of pick-up and drop-off of my daughter. but she does not call to talk to me. of course i in turn do not call to talk to her either. whenever i call her, the tone of her voice changes when she realizes it's me. i get the feeling that she doesn't like the sound of my voice. that she wishes there was some other way to communicate with me. she seems annoyed whenever we interact. this leaves me feeling like i have no mother. like the link that connected us as parent and child, mother and daughter, disintegrated and all i'm left with is the memory. like the blood that once flowed between us has been tainted.

> ** feeling the need to expand, analyze, dissect & correct all the issues housed in this piece, my desire is to continue to write it. my goal is to exorcise the demons lurking between the lines. however, realizing this pain continues, accepting the loss of the maternal bonds & claiming my right to feel what i feel when i feel, this piece ends.*

The Woman in Me
by Roxane Gay

Dear Mama,

   This is a letter that you will probably never read, but I have to
write it anyway. There are so many things I want to say. It's hard
to find the right words because I don't know how to justly
describe what I feel for you.
   I don't think you realize just how much you mean to me. You
are my mother. You are the ideal of the woman I would like to
become. You embody the type of woman I want to spend the rest
of my life with. You are the strongest and wisest person I know.
   There have been times when we've disagreed, but you are
always there for me. You know when to be a friend and when I
need a parent. When I was a little girl, you were the one waiting
for me when I ran home from school. No matter how busy you
were, you took the time to listen to all the little stories that kids
have after eight hours in school. When I cried, you were there to
dry my tears. When I was upset, you were the one who tried to
find out what was wrong. It's those things that I remember most.
   I don't think anyone knows me as well as you do. You know
me better than I know myself. That's scary sometimes, but you
are my mother, after all.
   I know life wasn't always easy. It was damn hard raising a
family in an all-white area. You had few friends, and there were
no people "like us" for miles around. I can't begin to imagine
how lonely that must have been.
   In a homogenous environment, you gave my brothers and I
our cultural identity. We've always known that we are Haitian.
You spoke French and Creole with us, so that we would know
our native language. At times it was frustrating not knowing how
to answer you. You always chuckled when we defiantly replied
in English.
   You taught us our heritage, everything about where we come
from. You taught us pride. When I came home complaining that

245

my teacher had told the class that Haitian people carry AIDS, you were fairly calm. The next day, you took me to school and taught my class and the teacher the true history of Haiti. After that, the school hired you as a French teacher.

Everyone who meets you is impressed with your knowledge. I loved bringing you to show and tell and stating with pride, "This is my Mommy."

As a child I took my culture for granted. I don't think I understood what it meant, but as an adult I am forever grateful for the things you've taught me.

I've always known that I am a lesbian, and I think you've always known, too.

It's been a difficult and guilt-wracked process reconciling my cultural and sexual identities. Haitian culture is very unaccepting of homosexuality. Gays and lesbians are seen as weak of character. I've always wanted to be a daughter you could be proud of, so I struggled a great deal with being gay.

I know I'm supposed to live life for myself, but most everything I do, I do with your approval in mind.

For a long time I tried to be straight Mom, but I can't do it. It's not fair to me and I deserve peace of mind, even if it's at your expense.

I know that doesn't seem fair, but this is who I am.

You've always taught me to be myself. Well, this is me. It breaks my heart to hurt you like this, but I hope that one day you will understand why I am who I am.

As a kid you told me that if one of us kids were gay, it would kill Dad. I now know that you were referring to yourself as well.

I spent many a night fantasizing about girls and every Wednesday I would repent my sins in confession. After the priest gave me penance, I prayed my little heart out begging God for absolution. I wanted him to save my wicked lesbian soul. My young mind was convinced that I was going straight to hell. I rationalized that in asking for forgiveness, I would be forsaken to a lengthy stay in purgatory instead. Catholic/Haitian angst is quite the lethal combination, as you well know.

When I finally came out to you, I felt a huge sense of relief. It was one less secret between us, and I know that we have gotten a lot closer. At first, you told me that you never wanted to meet my girlfriends. You didn't want to hear about the lifestyle I "chose" to lead.

I must say Mom, you've come a long way since then. Now we can talk about things I'm feeling. You meet my girlfriends and have plenty to say about which women aren't good enough for your only daughter.

I understood after first coming out that you needed time to mourn. You sure did a whole lot of mourning for the daughter you were losing, and for the dreams that were lost. Gone was the big wedding and me in the flowing white dress. Gone was the perverse pleasure you took in grilling eager boyfriends. Gone were the visions of baby-sitting grandchildren.

In time, you will realize that new dreams will replace those you have lost. I plan on getting married to a woman some day. I still want a family. My sexuality doesn't erase maternal instinct. I can only hope that I will be as good a mother to my children as you were to me.

The most important thing you've taught me is unconditional love. For many years I was terrified that you would turn your back on me, that you would hate me because of who I am. I appreciate the respect and acceptance you have extended to me. Too many of my friends have been rejected because of their sexuality. If only all parents could love their children unconditionally, life would be much easier for the gay and lesbian community.

I don't know how the rest of the family will react. I can only hope that they can be as open-minded as you. I am proud to be a Haitian woman and I am proud to be a Haitian lesbian. I can be both and it doesn't make me less of a woman than everyone else.

The woman in you is the woman in me. The strength of a woman, the sorrows of a woman, the passion of a woman and her pain. I am her. She is me.

The Words I Know, the Way I Understand
by Tonia Bryan

These are the words I know: lesbian, queer, gay, vagina, cunnilingus, Church and Welsley, Pride Day, IWD; words I have taken b(l)ack: wicca, bulla, sodomite, poum-poum, poonani, pussy suckin', hurrican season, Crop Over, ackee (the bajan kind), fish cake, extended and chosen family, Africa, Middle Passage, Barbados, Home; things I have woven into my life: eating pussy smelling strong of musk and cinnamon, making sweet bread and black cake on holidays, my right arm stiff and sore from wrestling with a full pot of coocoo, the feel of the word BAJAN as it rolls off my tongue, the sound of the name WICCA when she calls OUT to my soul.

I am coming out in/to realization of mySELF. I came out lacking knowledge; I was maybe all of twenty-three years old. There was more history in me than I allowed myself to see. There were more people holding up my insides than I could admit.

Touching, kissing, fucking *HER*, I was gathered up into the arms of our mothers. We licked and finger fucked, cumin' ecstatically into a no-woman's land of unspoken desires. I found the spot, the wet, fertile place between our clits, our culture and our past. I came home for the first time.

Her fingers filled me up, filled me with lost pieces of my past. I remember ... the first night we lay in bed where I had placed myself hoping she would fuck my brains out. For six hours we talked, giggled and shared, not touching, on extreme opposite sides of her futon. Two Black bajan wiccas choking on our shyness, unable to cross the chasm between desire and passion realized.

Me: "You know my uncle Jean the barber?"

Her: "*Your* father is Jean's brother? He used to cut my father's hair years ago. Everybody knows Jean."

Me: "I don't. I remember him from the last time I went to Barbados. I have a picture of him, though." This was a beginning for us, but especially for me. I was becoming ... She doesn't make me fried flying fish with enough pepper to make my eyes run water anymore. When you're both striving to be the other person's mother/ lover/ sister/ healer and protector, the closeness becomes too much.

* * * * *

I still crave the sight and sound of my sistren gathered in love and struggle, though. In my mind's eye, there's a good place where we're all talkin' at once. There's life-saving variety here. Differences of fashion, food, taste and sexual practice are honoured, not reviled. We get more excited, our eyes brighten. And the laughter? Our laughter combined breaks all sound barriers, does a two-step on top of our pain and the funky chicken on our internalized hatred of ourselves. Our words become a sweet cacophony of creative self-expression. In the fiery glare of our emerging spirits we are continually burnt to a crisp and remade with hope. We are West Indian lesbians of African descent and when we come home, culture, joy and pain seep out through our pores like sweat.

Around them and sometimes in my writing I use my own hybrid chat, a shaky mixture of Barbadian, Jamaican patois learned from the kids I grew up with, urban Black folk talk and whiter than white canadian speak. One of them says I'm looking *maga* and asks if I'm losing weight. A chorus of sucked teeth speaks volumes about our love of big wimmin, round hips, soft, yielding flesh and high, fat butts. This is something I came to appreciate, but not before my socialized love of scrawny bodies cost me the trust of my first love.

They cradle me in a familiar intensity of emotion, understanding my words and the untongued spaces too. There's loudness and exuberance here but none of the accusations I often hear in "wimmin of colour" or white spaces about violent, Black, West Indian wimmin who are too rude, intimidating and unsubtle to be tolerated. I don't have to hold back. I can breathe deeply, taking in the smell of sweaty arm pits, just-fucked pussy and freshly oiled hair. I hold tight onto flesh and feel strong forearms wrapped 'round me; their soft, thick lips brush my cheeks in greeting. I'm alive as I can only be with them.

250

I fear this, or more correctly I fear the temporariness of it. I fear the times when we are together because this unfailingly leads me to the times when we are not. Forces me to acknowledge the reality of being on my own, without someone to guard my back, when I stand trembling with just the memory of our togetherness to get me through the night. I live a half-life where I feel unwhole, only half a woman, part wicca, only a little Bajan and slightly African when I am not with them.

The courage of vulnerability is needed for me to form links with them and our herstory. Away from the context they provide, thoughts are hard to form and my mouth has trouble shaping the words we usually share. I feel that loss everytime we say goodbye, everytime a relationship or friendship ends.

Taking my place among them is about opening up, about letting them flow deep inside me, allowing them to stroke and savour the places where my soul is stored. Long-buried, precious memories of my grandmother's house in Barbados rise from that place. I remember learning to braid hair there. So many wimmin — my grandmother, my mother, sister, aunts and the wimmin who lived in and around Ashdeane Village taught me most of what I know. Not since the age of eight, since I left Barbados, left all that behind, have I felt so understood and so exposed.

So often I find myself searching for insubstantial glimmerings of wimmin from my past, my mother or sister in the faces and curves of Black lesbians I know now. This one has my sister's big, sad eyes. That one standing tall reminds me of my aunts in their youth. Tears of rememberance and the shrill laughter of childhood mingle and cavort near the surfce of my will.

I fear and admire the ways the adult and the child in me are reflected in their gaze. Am I home yet? Can I rest now? I need to. But I struggle with this unfamiliar, uncertain intimacy; it's been so long. And I don't want to get accustomed to something that may not be in my life tomorrow. I've mourned the loss of family for nineteen years; whether I'm talking about chosen, extended or biological family, grief and loneliness are never far away.

My sisters' clear-eyed view of my Black-skinned lesbian self scrapes uncomfortably at the armour I wear; sovereign boundaries are crossed too often for comfort. The cyclic ebb and flow of our lives — together then apart, together, apart ... feels too much like abandonment. And I'm not brave enough to risk that again; the cynic inside can't open herself to love unquestioningly anymore. Instead I seek the consistency and stability of solitude. Caught up in the grip of self-imposed isolation I wonder: Will I continue to remember who I am? Who will comb my hair and massage out muscles knotted tight with unexpressed emotion? Who will remember my true name and bury me when I am dead?

This Is Not Done
by Michele Hunter

One

It began during an innocent, unsuspecting meeting with my professor after class. "Shall we have coffee?" he said to me. "Sure," I responded, "how about the Red Cat?"

Settling into the small, campus cafe-of-convenience, Prof. Conrad and I continued our discussion about authenticity spurred by questions of races and nations. "Judith Butler's analysis seems to argue that authenticity is always linked to historical discursive constructions ... and the very mimicry of such 'authentic' identities can be interpreted as subversive. Are you familiar with her work?" I said to him, glibly, both struck and proud of my ability to pass as a straight woman although all of my thoughts were indeed feeling quite lesbian. As he responded, I watched this white man who found race so fascinating a subject of study, his eyes communicating his fascination with gender, give this answer:

"Well, I tend to think of Judith Butler's work as overly theoretical in nature, so I've avoided it."

I promised to lend him a copy of one of her shorter articles, for my sake, and we then changed the subject.

Throughout the conversation, I spoke openly about my interests in feminist studies and women's literature, sitting comfortably in my chair — or as comfortably as any young woman can sit under the gaze of her male professor — expounding on this or that theorist, taking into consideration this or that issue, always keeping in mind the importance of maintaining a respectful smile and emitting a convincing laugh.

253

In the middle of the conversation, he asked:

"Have you ever heard of Nicole Brossard?"

Since I hadn't, he recommended that I look at her work, "She's French Canadian and you would probably find her interesting," he urged.

About thirty minutes later, our meeting ended and we said our good-byes.

As I walked way, I thought nothing of our conversation, except that I suspected he had many affairs with women of color, and I could possibly be the next one. Feeling rejected by my last lover, this didn't seem so terrible.

Two

Early evening on the telephone with my friend, a wealth of lesbian-feminist knowledge.

"I am trying to write a queer interpretation of a book and I am not sure what to look at as far as models. Do you have any suggestions?"

"You might try *Lesbian Philosophies,* there's some good stuff in there..."

Without much effort, I found it at the library. In the dim and dusty stacks, I opened the book and looked over the table of contents. There was Nicole Brossard's name! I turned to the end and found two of her prose poems. "She's a lesbian!" I said to myself, almost loud enough for someone to hear me in those quiet stacks. "She's a lesbian, and he knows!"

I stood in the stacks dumbfounded. He had outwitted me. I couldn't even pass, anymore. Ever. I felt like I had been had. And we didn't even sleep together.

Three

As Prof. Conrad's course proceeded, I privately lamented and grew frustrated by the lack of lesbian writers. We finally came to the "week on women," the popular treatment of women's writing in literature courses, and he assigned one short story by a woman writer for each of us to present. He assigned Michelle Cliff's "Columba" to me.

That same day, my French language teacher told me that things weren't working out. She said that she thought that my French really wasn't all that bad, it was what I wanted to say that was difficult. What was difficult, I thought, was that she could not teach me this vocabulary. We determined that I should discuss alternatives and options with the department chair.

Four

I met with the chair the next day, full of apologies for arriving a few minutes before the end of his office hours. "I had a class..." I muttered apologetically.

I explained to him that I wanted out of the language class, that it was geared to freshmen and I wasn't learning anything.

"So, you think the course is beneath you?"

"Well, in a manner of speaking." What else could I say?

He wasn't satisfied.

255

"She tells me that you aren't turning in the work, that you come to class and scoff at the discussion and material— "

"That I have an attitude problem? That's ridiculous." Why did people have to be so predictable? I thought.

"Well, what is it? Why aren't you turning in the work?"

"When I do, she doesn't understand what I'm trying to say!" I bit my lip, hoping the tears wouldn't enter this man's office. I explained that it really wasn't my French, it really wasn't my damned French, it was what I was writing.

"But, why aren't you coming to class?"

He persisted and I broke. "You don't understand what it's like! The material [I couldn't say the teacher — I wish I had] is racist, sexist, classist, and homophobic: all under the guise of so-called French culture! I cannot learn anything in this type of environment! I have just seen too much — I am too old for this— " I think I had raised my voice at this point, because he looked uncomfortable in his chair. He did, however, manage to say,

"OK, OK, I understand — I mean, I could *never* really *understand...*" Then, repositioning himself in his chair, he said, "I probably shouldn't tell you this, but my wife is a South Asian woman. Although she is much, much older than you, I have observed her confront certain things and *often* she is justified in what she finds offensive. However, I think that when people talk of wanting to defend themselves they are still confronting unresolved issues within themselves...."

We spoke for another few minutes about exorcising old ghosts and how I should definitely drop the class. And how no one would have to change except me.

Five

I walked out of the building and the tears came.

Six

I decided that home would be the best place for me to go, almost shaking in disbelief that, by mentioning homophobia, I had just come out to the head of my department. As soon as I got there, I immediately got into bed and opened up the collection of short stories we were reading and looked for "Colomba."* I found it and tried to lose myself and the day in it.

I didn't know anything about the story except that since my teacher knew I was a lesbian, there was probably a gay subtext to it somewhere. I didn't know this for sure, but I did feel that this was his little test for me. (And my little test for him.) All I knew about Michelle Cliff was that she wrote about race and gender and feminism. You know, the same old stuff.

A servant for the narrator's family and close friend of the narrator, Colomba is baptized by an exiled priest convicted of being a pedophile. Marked by the priest's past and named after a white bird (a colin), Colomba seeks refuge on the land surrounding the house in a secret place, an old car inhabited by hundreds of white doves, many or all of which he has named. A few are introduced, with great respect and fondness on the part of the young boy.

Shortly afterwards, the narrator's caretaker, a greedy aunt, hears of the "bounty" and decides the birds must all be killed. Respon-

---

* From *Green Cane and Juicy Flotsam: Short Stories by Caribbean Women*. Carmen C. Esteves and Lizabeth Paravisini-Gebert, Eds. Rutgers U.P. 1991.

sible for all of the household duties, Colomba is instructed to murder the doves as well. The narrator finds him in the car, crying and breaking their necks, one by one. "Sorry man, you hear?" he says.

The tears come, again, more plentifully and loudly.

Seven

I read the story every single day before my presentation, crying each time and trying to figure out what I could possibly say about it. I expected that this story commanded a queer reading that only a queer could do. Although this was tempting, I wasn't fully prepared to do it in class. I returned to the library, hoping for some answers. A couple of recent interviews with Michelle Cliff were readily available. My only hope.

I photocopied one to read later that night.

The tone of the interview was an open one. In the middle of it, Cliff stated that she could not come into herself without writing, that she had written through the many issues surrounding her identity in her books. She spoke about class, race and gender and how she had only come to resolve certain issues and aspects around her identity by writing about it.

She also stated (for the first time?) that she is a lesbian.

I read this over and over, while forcing myself to continue reading.

Eight

The morning of my presentation, I considered how Cliff's

autobiographical information might shed some light on the meanings of the story, how she was dealing with being out as a writer, and how difficult it was for her to be open about her lesbian identity after years of rejection from her community because of her light skin color. (I suspected this latter issue could have been an alternative incentive for my teacher to pick me, the fairest of them all, to present it.)

The conclusion will probably be a disappointment. As I expected, eight people were to give (in)complete synopses of their stories in less than five minutes' time. I don't even remember what I said about "Colomba," except that I never read from the interview and, the day of my presentation, I never came out to the class.

Nine

In her interview, Michelle Cliff said something about going crazy if she were to consider her audience as she was writing. Writing, she claimed, was a process that was for *her* more than anyone else.

In writing something that I could not bury inside me, I have begun something of my own. Something *to* me *from* me.

This is not done.

this lesbian poem

by akhaji zakiya

this lesbian poem
is for all those sistas
who wonder ... what   2   women   do
& for all those who know
the endless possibilities

this lesbian poem
takes her place as *part of the family*
she is a
butch/fem/
single/involved/married/open/
monogamous/
just curious
and respectful of the many ways we be
kind of poem

one

this lesbian poem
is a dyke of the 90s
but she ain't no
alternative advertising trick

she isn't fooled
by propped up media pseudo-lesbo hype
posing vague, trendy couplings of
sister?   daughter? mother?   friend?

this lesbian poem
been loving women
since before it was
h o t
she a 24/7 dyke
who's gonna take her 15 minutes
of fleeting fame

and keep on steppin'

two

this lesbian poem
is for the sistas who try
to wash away their pain
with the blood of others ...

tired
of the popular power games
insecurities, fear and past horror
turned nasty ...
acting out
and scarring deep

this lesbian poem
will <u>not</u>
kick you in the gut,
sex you against your will,
slap you across the room
or
call you a ugly, worthless piece of shit

this lesbian poem
will dance
to the beat of your clit
fuck you sweet without force
in this violent world
as she struggles to love
herself
and you

three

resisting
the dirt and disrespect
of internalized hate ...

this lesbian poem
is out in the life
maturing
with the responsibility
of her personal power

this lesbian poem
joins the flow
of pieces by pussy-sucking sistas
everywhere
testifyin' 'bout our movements,
sanctifyin' our unions,
solidifyin' our resistance,

as dawn cracks
this mutha/   cunt
will express her sexuality
wide open & in colour
even after
she is born again

untitled
by Nailah Taliba Tulinegwe

Well, it's about going down memory lane when "coming out" is mentioned.

I came into myself when, after a satisfying relationship with my boyfriend who was a college jr. while i was in h.s., I realized that my attraction to women was stronger. I knew, given the chance, how I could make her feel because I knew how I wanted to feel.

When I enrolled in a dental course, my energies were to get through the course (I later taught dental courses to some wonderful students years later). Met this older woman, we talked. Went to a gospel program. Many members of a prominent choir were "family." She remarked after seeing the brothas flaming, "what makes them that way?" Well, in all of my 17 yr. old wisdom, I said it was a state of being, knowing how one wants to relate intimacy and receive the same with the same sex.

She said she never had experienced that but should she want to, she wanted me to be the first. Well, after I did the adolescent thang (dream and cream...) we finally got together and it was all that! From that point on, I was involved with older women, taking them to concerts, grocery stores, etc. or just talking. My twin sister asked me why were all of these strange (unfamiliar voices ... certainly not those of schoolmates!) women calling ME? Then she asked, "Are they 'funny'? Are you?" When she heard my reply, she said, "I love you no matter what!"

Moms was not happy and made it a point to ask me about EVERY gay-related issue she could find! When Marlon Riggs' *Tongues Untied* was aired, I had totally forgotten about it. She said she heard a (white) radio evangelist talk about his young son watching something disgusting on tv. I said, well maybe it's cable. She said no, the minister said network tv about men

kissing men. Now, I was in the kitchen washing dinner dishes
while she was at the table finishing dessert during this exchange.
Slow me, still didn't get it until she asked, "Yeah, men kissing
men... do YOU know anything about THIS?!" Well! I said, "no."
Then it dawned on me what in the world she was talking about!
Hindsight said, "Sure I do. I helped FUND this effort! Of
COURSE, I know what you're talking about!" yeah, right! I
voluntarily had my teeth pulled and only the third molars!

Pops was cool and liked all of the lovers I took home for them to
see. Moms adopted the military stance, "Don't ask, don't tell." I
respect her for knowing where her tolerances are. She loves me
but always knew she had twins who were night and day even
though identical in appearance. Yeah, we even dressed alike until
she got married. Then our wardrobes changed! But, hey! I really
came out because there was no one else to be with and share
with. I was more introverted while my twin sister was extro-
verted. I wouldn't go to the store without her!

When she told me she was getting married, I knew for my own
survival I had to make adjustments. And they weren't difficult.
Just a coming into my own thing. I became "unmousey" by
changing my clothes, image and seeing what potential laid
within. I knew how I wanted to look, and when the inward
person was happy, the outward followed.

There have been co-workers from various jobs I felt comfortable
about coming out to. And all responses were, "and does THAT
change the person we've come to know or your job performance?" Real supportive folks the Creator has placed in my path
during this life for which I am grateful!

That was 24 yrs ago and my twin and I are still closer than ever
and she still loves me! My relational experiences with women of
color and one with a white woman were very enlightening
indeed. No regrets, no negatives... all for my learning.

I've matured and grown sensitive even more to needs of others as well as myself. Since that time, I realized that after my father's death and my living with an unfaithful lover of 8 yrs, I knew I would survive and succeed in whatever my endeavors were. Hence, Nailah (one who succeeds).

I have and I will continue...

untitled (4/'91)
by Renita Martin

"it ain't nat'ral
just ain't nat'ral, jesus said"
say some sisters who
choose to talk still
after i tell them

some peers admire my
open/mind/deadness like
i *acquired* a taste for
my existence
was not born loving
but love women mechanically

while some brothers say i am
politically in-
correct that i one
woman must "build the nation
be fruitful and multiply. jesus said."

sometimes i feel like
the cigarette
butt i hold on to
walking down the street
      usefulness exhausted cannot
      be thrown on the ground to
      defy nature
      or in the garbage to
      start a fire
like my jesus had
nowhere to lay
lay his head.
sometimes i wonder why
they don't have ashtrays
on the street or why i
don't just start a fire.

Waiting to Exhale: Interview with Gina Taylor
by Denise A. Moore

[Gina Taylor is a pseudonym for a woman who is an exotic dancer living in New Orleans.]

Denise Moore: What does it mean to be an "out" lesbian, to you?

Gina Taylor: What it means to me is to be able to be proud of who you are, what you are, and not have to answer to anybody for your actions or what you feel.

DM: Lesbian feelings?

GT: Well, any feelings at all. In my mind, we live in a society where everybody has to explain every single thing that they do. I mean, at my house, ever since I was a kid, you get up to take a piss, and you hear, "Where you going?" "What you doing?" To not have to answer to anybody and be happy with yourself, I mean.

DM: Do you have a significant event or series of events that illustrate what your coming out experience was? What happened to make you think you were out?

GT: My first real girlfriend.

DM: What happened? Just having a girlfriend?

GT: No, because I had had a girlfriend before her, but when she came along it was totally different. It wasn't like experimentation, or I'm ashamed to be seen out with her because I don't know what people will think. I wasn't really that much into my first girlfriend.

DM: So, what event? Was there a thing that happened that made you feel like, "OK, I'm an out lesbian now"?

GT: Knowing that she was an out lesbian, and still is. I would have to feel totally uncomfortable being stuck in the closet, knowing that when we go somewhere together, she wants to caress, hold hands, etc., and I can't because I'm ashamed. She made me feel comfortable, realize that what I was wasn't a bad thing, wasn't a wrong thing. She just made me feel like a whole person.

DM: What was the girl, woman, like who was your first love?

GT: Oh, boy! My first? She was a trip, to put it mildly. I went to school with her for a while, and I was seeing a guy at the time. I got into it with him, and I considered her a good friend, so I called her on the phone one day and got to talking about it, and I told her, I said, "Well, I've had it up to here. I'm sick and tired of being sick and tired. I'm either gonna become a nun, a hermit or a lesbian." And she said, "Well, I don't know if you know this or not, but I'm a lesbian." I was like, "Get the hell outta here!" She said, "No, no, really! And I've always been attracted to you." And I was like, "Oh, hell." So it just pretty much flew on its own from there. It didn't end up being anything good, though.

DM: What did she do that attracted you to her?

GT: The simple fact that she was open, she was very persistent. Dominant. And she was very, very beautiful.

DM: Where you seduced, or was your first same-sex encounter considered mutual experimentation?

GT: It was mutual.

DM: Experimentation?

GT: Well, yeah, I guess you would consider it experimentation.

DM: What happened?

GT: I was at her house one day, and we had just come back from a club that they used to have over on Claiborne called Lexus. We had had a nice time, had a few drinks, and we came back to her house, got comfortable. One thing led to another, and the next thing I knew, it was on! I wasn't really sure what to do or anything; I didn't know what to do. I really didn't know what I was doing until my first true love came along.

DM: Are there any particular character or personality traits that attract you to women?

GT: Yeah.

DM: What are they?

GT: Well, you mean what I look for in a woman?

DM: Is there anything in particular about women that attracts you?

GT: Just the simple fact that they are women! Hair, face, body, smell, the way they walk, the way they talk, the fact that they get PMS just like me every month. I mean, I've always been attracted to women!

DM: What is butch?

GT: Cool! (laughter)

DM: I take it you like butch?

GT: Yes, I do, I really do! I don't know what it is that makes me so attracted to butch women. I just think they are so-o-o sexy!

DM: What is butch?

GT: To me, it's an attitude. It's the way they dress, they way they carry themselves, the way they walk, talk, etc.

DM: How do butch women dress?

GT: I saw one particularly cute one with a thermal shirt on, some baggy jeans and lumberjack boots! Then she wore a baseball cap occasionally! She was real cute! Umm!

DM: What is femme?

GT: Femme is what I consider myself to be.

DM: Describe yourself.

GT: Hmmm. Well, I'm real prissy. I don't leave the house without cosmetics, if I can help it. I mean, I won't even go to the mailbox without cosmetics on. I never know when I'm going to run into somebody famous or not. I mean, who knows, I might go to get my mail one day and run into Melissa Etheridge or something.

DM: I guess that answers my other question. Do you feel these terms describe you?

GT: Oh, yeah, I'm very fish. Excuse me, femme. I couldn't be butch if I wanted to.

DM: Why not?

GT: It's just... I can't. I'm so prissy, and my nails have to be done, and the hair. You know.

DM: What's the best thing a lover ever said to you?

GT: The best thing? Well, I've only had one true lover in my life, and I think the best thing she ever said to me was that even though I had a few character flaws here and there, that I was still somebody, and that I'd still make something out of myself and get somewhere in life.

DM: How do you feel about men in general?

GT: I think men are like trees. Trees and bushes and shrubs. They're pretty much there. I don't have a whole hell of a lot of use for them, but they're OK to look at.

DM: Sounds like something I'd say! Have you ever had a male lover?

GT: A long time ago, when I was trying to please everybody else but myself. That's how I ended up with a 3-year-old right now.

DM: Is that why you had a male lover? To please everybody else?

GT: Yeah, that's the reason why.

DM: Who knows you're a lesbian?

GT: Oh, God, a shitload of people know! I live with my sister. She tries her best to pretty much avoid the whole topic if she can. But she knows something ain't right. She comes into my room and I have Penthouse magazines and stuff laying around. She's not gonna ask me, "Are those your articles?" Of course they're mine; they're in my room! She sees all the gay and lesbian paraphernalia I have sitting around, and she knows about my first true girlfriend, my first true love, so she knows something ain't right.

DM: Who doesn't know?

GT: A shitload of people don't know, too.

DM: Why?

GT: Well, I have parents who are old. My dad will be 73 soon, my mother's in her late 60s, and they're not feeling physically well these days. I have grandparents that... let's just say they would be totally heartbroken if they knew that "I was like that." Not that I don't want to not say anything to them, but for the simple fact that not to kick up dust, and make things any more difficult than it has to be. I keep my private life to myself, and whatever they do, that's their business.

275

DM: The next question is the title of this book: "Does Your Mother Know?"

GT: Does my mother know? Hmm. My mother knows, but she doesn't know. She knows in her heart, but her mind, when she's looking me dead in my face, won't let her realize what's really there.

DM: Do you think it's more difficult to be out in the African-American community?

GT: Yes.

DM: Why?

GT: Well, because brothers and other sisters that aren't gay, they have a tendency to look down upon lesbians for what we are. I don't know exactly how to say this. The first thing they holler is, "Oh, that's something the white man put on 'em, or made 'em do. They trying to be like them white girls," or whatever. And brothers have a tendency to just get totally mad when they see two beautiful black women walking down the street holding hands together, because it's like, "Well, what, you can't find a brother that's good enough for you?" or whatever. They don't like it.

DM: Describe your dream lover.

GT: She would be about 5'8", about 150-155, nice shape. Butch. She would have to kick the baseball caps, the plaid shirts, jeans and the lumberjack boots at least four or five times a week. She would have to be smart. Not so much refined, because I can take somebody to be ignorant with me once in a while. It's boring if you don't have any fun! She'd have to know what she wants in life. Pretty much be the man, so to speak. Not that I want a man, because I don't. Like I said, that's like growing dandelions and weeds and shit in your back yard. I want a woman who can do just as much for me as a man thinks that he can. I want her to bring home the bacon, fry it up in a pan, and all the fun stuff. I

276

don't mind being Susie Homemaker. She would have to be pretty much everything. I'm probably asking for a whole hell of a lot, but I'm sure there's someone out there who can live up to it.

DM: What kind of lesbian relationship would you like in a perfect world?

GT: Oh, God! A woman with no problems. Maybe one here or there; something's wrong if you don't have any problems at all — everybody knows that. Just one with no problems! I mean, if you don't have any problems in the relationship, then everything pretty much falls into place.

DM: What kind of problems?

GT: Shit, anything! From being able to get along half of the time and not getting along the other half of the time, or family that doesn't want you with that particular person. Any number of things — having a job that the other person doesn't like, or personality flaws; they just should be able to handle it. You don't break up with a person or get out of a relationship just because you don't like one or two things about them. If there was such a thing as a "perfect" relationship, I'd have one with no problems at all. Maybe one or two, but hardly anything. No significant problems.

DM: What are your specific political concerns?

GT: To be totally honest with you, I'm pretty much drifting here and there. I try my best not to concern myself with things that I don't have a whole hell of a lot of control over. Don't get me wrong; I vote when I have to vote, and I voice my opinion on this and that, but as far as political concerns go, I don't really have that much to say about it.

DM: What are your specific social concerns?

GT: Crazy, deranged, prejudiced lunatics that don't understand that two people can fall in love and it's not their fault that one of them happens to have the same genitalia as the other.

DM: Homophobia.

GT: Um-hmm.

DM: What are your specific economic goals?

GT: I want to be rich! No, I'm kidding. I don't want to be rich; I just want to be comfortable. I don't want to have to want for anything, so to speak.

DM: Do you have any children?

GT: Yes, I do; I have one.

DM: How would you like the children in your life to view your lifestyle?

GT: Well, I don't want to hide anything from them. You can only hide things so long as it is anyway. Whatever's in the dark is gonna come out in the light. I could stay in the closet all the time if I wanted to, but eventually somebody's gonna see me sticking a foot out or something, you know?

DM: Waiting to exhale!

GT: Yeah, waiting to exhale! But as far as the kids go; I have four brothers and four sisters. I'm number 9. I got nieces and nephews coming out of the side of my neck, if you want the truth, and then I have one. Some of my nieces and nephews know what's going on with me and they accept it. They're fine with it. The way they see it is, well auntie, whatever you're doing in the room with the door shut, we don't know about it anyway, so what difference does it make? And I think that's a pretty mature view for kids. The older ones, the younger ones, they pretty much all think the same. The very young children, I try not to say very much to them; if they ask, I'll try and explain it the best I can. My little girl, right now, she's 3. She's a really smart kid to be so young. She's not stupid at all; she's very, very bright. She pretty much knows if something's up with me or not. I mean, she wasn't really around my true love very much, but when she was around her, she knew that there was something special between us. Kids have a way of sensing things, and they take a lot more in than we give them credit for.

DM: If you had to give one solid piece of advice to a young black woman questioning her sexuality, what would it be?

GT: The first thing I'd tell them is don't jump into anything that you're not sure of, because you'll be sorry later, but for the most part, just keep in mind that you have all the time in the world. Think about your options, what you feel like is deep inside of you, and take it from there. There's no law that says you have to do one thing or another. A woman may or may not be a lesbian; she may very well be bi. It's just within her to figure out what the hell she is and take it from there.

we will not talk about this
by Eva Yaa Asantewaa

we will not talk about this,
over our waffles and chocolate and apricots,
that a whiff of spice,
rising from your skin,
is sufficient,
that my hands find their way
along your rosy, plump contours,
under your husband's merry eyes.
as if fingers were villagers
on their way to carnival.
we won't talk about this
or about my first time with your husband
and how, since then, you nudge me towards him
when i am already high on musk and talc,
the silk route of your thighs,
and want nothing more than more
hours of you,
or about how your husband slithers out of me,
and he and i slip away to our respective corners,
resting for a new round that never comes.
what can we talk about then?
we can be nice about this.
we can all pull on our blue jeans, comb our hair,
eject my ruben blades from your stereo,
step out into the straight, white streets of east side summer,
and not talk about this.
i come out, under the sun, your initiate,
already deep in mermaid's music.
you have given me myself,
and, of that, we will not speak,
but do tell your husband to revise his plans.
i am going.
how soon will you follow?

When I Was a Little Girl
by Lena-Nsomeka Gomes

Everyone had a name for me after I came out. Bulldagger, Butch, Dyke, Lesbian, Lesbo, Gay, Homosexual, Homo, Queer. My entire identity was defined by strangers and summed up in a single word, like an object. I managed to survive those confusing times by remembering the innocent years, when my love for women had no name.

I didn't have a name for myself when I was young. I thought it was just me. Sometimes I did think that God made a mistake. Maybe I was supposed to have been born a boy. I mean, how else could I explain all of my desires for girls?

When I was in third grade, I was completely in love with Ms. Sonnhalter. I used to bring her fresh-cut sunflowers, which I pulled out from a patch of grass on the way to school. She would smile lightly and tell me to get back in line. In class, I would watch her walk back and forth from the chalkboard to her desk. She was sexy and lovely. I wanted to kiss her in her mouth like the men did in the old-fashioned movies. I didn't think I could kiss her as a girl. Girls don't kiss girls. I didn't know why that was so.

After school, I would find a spot on top of her desk and she and I would talk for hours. She liked me. I was convinced that she was in love with me, too. I know it's crazy, I was just a kid, but I could tell by the way she looked at me.

One afternoon, a monitor came in our class and handed Ms. Sonnhalter a piece of white paper folded in the shape of an airplane. She opened it up as we were all taking our exams. I watched her from the top of my eyelids. She was smiling — a big, wide smile. The way I imagined her smiling for me one day.

After the exam was over, a big man walked in. He had a long pony tail and wore tiny glasses. His name was Mr. Henderson. As the class emptied out, he got closer and closer to Ms. Sonnhalter. I made my move and sat at my usual spot on her desk, but she told me I had to go home because she had a date with Mr. Henderson. "He teaches math in pod D. He's my boyfriend," she said.

He smiled and extended his rough hairy hands to me. Suddenly my head was on fire and my stomach was melting from all the warm blood gushing out of my heart like a waterfall.

From then on, I was Ms. Sonnhalter's worst nightmare.

I came into class late and interrupted her lesson plans. I cussed her out all the time and threw crumpled up pieces of paper at her. Each time she asked me to stay after class because she said she wanted to talk to me, I would yell at her in front of everybody. "I don't talk to white girls!" All the other kids — mostly black and Latino — laughed. Her beautiful face would get sad, but I didn't care. I was focused on punishing her for breaking my heart.

One afternoon, I called her a "prejudice white bitch!" That was it for her. She came over my parent's house that same night. In the living room, she sat with my dad. My mom was in the kitchen making tea.

My dad called me. I was terrified. My mom was behind me holding a silver tray filled with colorful cookies and beverages. "Hurry up and go answer your father," she said in a whisper.

They were all talking, but I was blinded by the sight of her. Can't you see my heart is aching? I sat there stupefied until my dad pushed my shoulder — "Answer me!" "Huh?" I mumbled, like someone in a stupor.

"Why are giving this nice lady a hard time?" he asked again. Then I got mad. She had betrayed me again. "Because...she's prejudice. She doesn't like me... cuz... I'm black." I was so ashamed after I said that because I knew it wasn't true, but what else was I supposed to say? That I was in love with her? That I dreamed about being her boyfriend?

Ms. Sonnhalter began asking me questions about racism and stuff like that. I couldn't hear her. I just watched her mouth coming at me and imagined our first kiss.

Then I felt a heavy, hot sensation on the side of my head. I guess my dad hit me, because the familiar sound of my mother pleading him to stop had begun. Ms. Sonnhalter looked upset and she asked my dad not to hit me, but suggested that he talk to me because she said I was smart. In fact, she said I was one of her smartest students.

She protected me! She thought I was smart? She does love me

after all!

Although I knew we could never be lovers, I took comfort in knowing that she loved me. At that moment, I promised everyone that I would behave myself, and I did. The rest of the school year I spent sitting on top of her desk, only this time we talked about Mr. Henderson and her other boyfriends. I was still in love with her and secretly hoped that one day she would tell me she wanted me and we would make passionate love all night long.

That day never came, but we were to remain friends for two decades later.

* * * * *

I got into this strange habit around my eleventh birthday. When my parents were out, usually food shopping, I would empty out my father's closet. I used to watch him intently as he meticulously folded and knotted his ties into a perfect shape and place his silk handkerchiefs in his suit pocket. I also paid close attention to most of his mannerisms, how he walked and talked, held a glass in his hand and smoked cigarettes. I practiced the same things when he was gone.

When their car pulled out of the driveway, I was off into the bedroom looking for an outfit. I laid the clothes out carefully on top of the bed. The suit jacket, pants, white cotton shirt and the tie. Then I went through his dresser and found jockey shorts and socks. After a few minutes, I stood in front of the mirror completely transformed. Of course, all the clothes didn't fit, but you really couldn't tell because I wore it with such pride. His shoes were definitely too big, but with three pairs of socks on, my feet stayed inside and I could manage to strut around the house.

I wet my hair, brushed it back and greased it down with Vaseline. Then I pulled out one of his cigarettes from beneath a neatly folded tablecloth inside the kitchen cupboard. My mother hid them from him because, she complained, he smoked too much. Then I went to the living room, turned on the radio and sat back on the sofa, smoking and pretending to be at a party, where all the pretty women were dancing around and checking me out.

I got up to dance with a few of them. They loved me. My

name was Tito, I would tell them charmingly. I dragged for years that way, convinced that the only way that I could ever love a woman was to become a man.

* * * * *

That was around the same time that the telephone calls began.

My brothers used to make prank calls at night while my parents were asleep. They sat by the phone with a telephone book, scouting for women's names. Then they dialed the numbers and waited. When a man answered, they hung up, but when a woman answered, they would call her dirty names and tell her, very graphically, how they wanted to fuck her. They would do this for hours until they grew tired and went off to bed.

They never seemed to run out of numbers. They asked me to join in and sometimes I did, but I always felt bad calling women those names and hurting their feelings, but I was very excited hearing their caring voices.

Something was awaking inside of my groin and I had no idea what it was, where it came from or what to call it. All I knew was that it felt incredible and I didn't want it to stop. So I started making my own telephone calls on their off nights.

Armed with the white pages in one hand and the telephone extended from the kitchen into the bathroom in the other, I leaned back on the toilet and made my calls. But my calls were different. I never offended the women; I just pretended to be a man who had the wrong number.

After I found a name I liked, I would dial her number and ask for another name. "Hi, can I speak with Lisa?" She would then tell me that I had the wrong number, but I would repeat her number back to her. "Really? Is this 282-5719?" Yes, she answered, "but there is no Lisa living here." Then I would say as charmingly as possible in a subtle, seductive tone, "I'm sorry. I was feeling a little lonely tonight. You sound very nice. Would you be interested in talking with me?" She would either hang up abruptly or say, "Alright, I have a few minutes."

If she agreed to talk with me, usually our conversations would last for several hours. I learned that most people have a lot in common. We think that we can't relate because of our differences, but once we get beyond the superficial, we realize we're all looking for the same things: love and acceptance.

My name was always the same — Tito — and I was seventeen, in my senior year. Luckily, I was blessed with a deep baritone voice. They were always older, usually between 19 and 40. I think they were just as lonely as I was; just as in need of a friend. I made them feel beautiful and special and they made me feel loved.

I told no one about the uncharted territory I was traveling. Each night as I prepared for the evening's conversations, a flurry of unfamiliar emotions would sweep through my entire body like an orgasmic wave. I was completely enthralled, titillated and obsessed with desire. I had crossed boundaries of gender and social constructs that I was not yet aware of. I never even thought it was necessary to question my sexuality: I was beyond sex. I was transformed, transfixed. I had met the waves and I was riding high on pure innocence.

My phone life lasted over a year. Although I spoke to most of the women only once, I did develop a few lasting relationships. There was Tracy, a 19-year-old college student, and Marie, a 38-year-old secretary who worked at a nearby clinic. I had fallen in love with them both. I even shared a favorite song with Marie, "The Side Show" by Blue Magic. We often sang it together and each time it played on the radio, I fantasized that I was making love to her under a huge weeping willow tree.

Sometimes I felt guilty about lying that I was a man, but I couldn't imagine telling them that I was a woman. I didn't want to lose them. I feared their rejection; their horror and disgust at learning the truth. I wasn't doing anything wrong, nor were they. We were simply people sharing our lives with strangers we had come to know intimately.

The phone calls ended one night in April after Tracy expressed her eagerness to meet me. She asked me to send her a picture. She said she wanted to put my voice to a face. I pulled out our family photo album and searched for one. At last, I found a portrait of my cousin, Christian. He was about 20 and very handsome.

A week later, when I called her, she was suddenly mad over

me. We flirted all the time, but this was different. "Why didn't you tell me how fine you were? I can't believe it! I want to go out on a date with you. Will you come to my house and pick me up?" Oh shit, I thought. "Sure, baby. I'll pick you up on Friday." For the next three nights I alternated between states of deep contemplation and irrational consideration.

I almost convinced myself that I could wear my father's suit, my brother's shoes and pull it off. I fantasized over and over in my head about how Friday night would be. I would ring her doorbell and she would come out dancing in the wind in her long dress with love-stained eyes. I even imagined cutting my long braids and painting on a slight goatee like Christian wears.

I studied his picture obsessively, trying to reconstruct my femaleness. Eventually I came to the acceptance that even if I was to fool her, it would only be for one night, because when the moment of intimacy arrived, she would discover that her telephone man was a thirteen-year-old girl. I couldn't call her anymore. What would I tell her?

The game had ended at that moment of truth. I knew Marie would someday have the same desire to meet me and I would not be able to fulfill her needs, either. It was over. I never called them again.

* * * * *

A few years later, at 15, I would find myself in a position of being forcibly pulled out of the closet, so to speak, by both my cousin Anna and my mother. Anna was an afro-wearing revolutionary social worker who counseled troubled youth in the community. She also participated in protests and marches and was always preaching about socialism and black politics. She was my hero.

One Sunday morning, at her kitchen table, she handed me my first adult book, *Our Bodies, Ourselves*. It was wrapped up in old newspaper. (She was heavily into recycling.) I flipped through it awkwardly. No one had ever given me a book before.

After a few minutes, the consciousness-raising moment came like rain out of a clear blue sky. She suggested that I turn to a

288

chapter titled "Sexuality." The subtitle, "Homosexuality." She sat back with a cup of coffee and a burning cigarette between her lips and said, "I think you're a lesbian. What do you think?"

I freaked out. I got up. I angrily told her that I didn't need her psychoanalysis. I denied being a lesbian.

I hated the sound of that word. It felt dirty and weird.

She listened calmly like a therapist who is more concerned with her ego than she is with my trauma. I slammed that dirty, shameful book down and walked out.

It was a hot summer day and the sun was cooking my back. Usually I take a bus when I visit her because she lives several miles away, but that morning I decided to walk back home. If I could have, I would have walked to the end of the earth than to name myself a lesbian.

Then it was my mother's turn. One cold winter night, my mother and I sat up watching television. There was no heat because my father had spent the money drinking. We were both cuddled together on the couch under an electric blanket. The TV show *Dallas* was on. That night's episode was about Steve Carrington, the gay son who came out to his father in a highly dramatic scene. Well, my mother decided to use this as her opportunity to coax me out. She searched my face and said, "You know, he's gay. That means he likes men."

I shrugged my shoulders. "It's TV, ma. He's not real." I moved away from her slightly.

She went on to say, "I know his father must be heartbroken to know his only son is gay. I often wonder if my only daughter is gay, too." Then she looked at me for an answer.

I got up and angrily said, "I'm not gay. I'm not a TV character! I'm real!" I slammed the door and left the room.

She never asked me again, but I knew she was convinced that I was a lesbian because she never stopped watching me, especially when I was in the company of women.

* * * * *

Later, everyone had a name for me. Bulldagger, Butch, Dyke, Lesbian, Lesbo, Gay, Homosexual, Homo, Queer. My entire identity is now defined by strangers and summed up in a single word, like an object. But I remember the innocent years, when my love for women had no name.

Without Thinking
by Liz Messerly

I was so accustomed to ignoring my gender and the color of my skin that I truly believed I was part of the white male-dominant family I grew up in. When I made faces in the mirror, I knew the eyes were mine, but I kept myself blind to the color of my skin. I forced myself to believe that as I got older my skin and hair would lighten and I would become a white boy.

Growing up as the only black person in a racist white and Latin family was very painful. I quickly learned not to be the individual I appeared to be. I wasn't allowed to have any black friends or wear my hair in any of the popular black styles of the '70s. Black slang was enough cause for a stern look and a fierce grip from my mother while she asked where I picked up that kind of language.

I knew that if the color of my skin was a tight-lipped issue, then the preference of my soul's desire would be bigger than just an issue. I was in the fourth grade and knew that my attraction to girls was something I should keep to myself, hoping the emotions would go away. I was literally the black sheep of the family and constantly reminded of it. Being any more different would have been too much to carry.

On one particular morning, I decided to leave for school a little early to play in the snow. But the slowly brewing sleet quickly put a stop to my idea. After arriving at school, I waited inside by a set of cast iron heaters with two friends. The heaters clanged and wheezed as if near death, but my friends and I paid no attention and began thumbing through teen heartthrob magazines.

The cover of one read "Farrah Fawcett Poster Inside!" in large orange letters. I tore through the pages, preteen perspiration on the tips of my fingers absorbing the ink, leaving heavy fingerprints. I was a Charlie's Angels junkie, and anything I could find with the Angels in it held my full attention.

I froze when I found my prize. Seeing Farrah with her overflowing blonde hair lolling over her tight taut T-shirt stunned me. Her glowing smile appeared to take up most of the page and I quickly drifted into my own private place of ecstasy.

I could hear her voice and laughter; she was interested in *me*. I pictured myself being a tall, blonde, blue-eyed stud with Farrah fawning over me. I was far away from where I was and could not hear my friends carrying on, nor the heaters clanging as if digesting some poisonous liquid.

Without thinking, I opened my mouth, and out rolled, "I love..."

The sound of my own voice woke me from my trance and I looked up at my friends. They had heard nothing and continued chattering without hesitation.

Knowing that I was about to admit through voice that I loved another girl struck my soul like an unexpected clap of thunder. Perspiration popped up on my forehead and began rolling down my temple. My voice and emotions all seemed so obscenely loud that I froze for a few seconds and wondered if it really happened.

The earth stopped that day. I stood next to those heaters for what seemed hours, nearly overheating at the thought of being so different. I was in shock knowing that my feelings were not going to just disappear. From that day forward I moved myself farther away from everyone in order to keep from voicing those feelings again.

You ask why I stayed married all those years
by mistinguette

Like water, love takes
the shape of what contains it:
cell, leaf
gourd, stream.
Runs wide or deep
to pass through barren places;
grows icy cold, and
sometimes disappears
underground.

Love, too
seeks its own level;
trace to lake,
like to like.
And a river will try
to flow uphill
in its sedulous race
to the sea

Selected Bibliography

Abbott, Deborah and Ellen Farmer. *From Wedded Wife to Lesbian Life: Stories of Transformation.* Freedom, CA: Crossing Press, 1995.

Adelman, Marcy, ed. *Long Time Passing: Lives of Older Lesbians.* Boston: Alyson Publications, 1986.

Anzaldúa, Gloria, and Cherríe Moraga, eds. *This Bridge Called My Back: Writings By Radical Women of Color.* New York: Kitchen Table: Women of Color Press, 1983.

Barber, Karen and Sarah Holmes, eds. *Testimonies: Lesbian Coming Out Stories.* Boston: Alyson Publications, 1988.

Bauer, Marion Dane, ed. *Am I Blue?: Coming Out from the Silence.* New York: HarperCollins, 1994.

Birtha, Becky. *Lovers' Choice.* Seattle: Seal Press, 1987.

Brown, Rita Mae. *Rubyfruit Jungle.* New York: Bantam Books, 1973, 1988.

Chandler, Kurt. *Passages of Pride: Lesbian and Gay Youth Come of Age.* New York: Times Books, 1995.

Clarke, Cheryl. *Experimental Love: Poetry.* Ithaca, NY: Firebrand Books, 1993.

_____. *Humid Pitch: Poetry.* Ithaca, NY: Firebrand Books, 1989.

_____. *Living as a Lesbian: Poetry.* Ithaca, NY: Firebrand Books, 1986.

Davis, Madeline S., and Elizabeth L. Kennedy. *Boots of Leather, Slippers of Gold: The History of a Lesbian Community.* New York: Penguin, 1993.

DeLaney, L. Joyce. and Catherine E. McKinley, eds. *Afrekete: An Anthology of Black Lesbian Writing.* New York: Anchor Books, 1995.

Due, Linnea. *Joining the Tribe: Growing Up Gay & Lesbian in the 1990s.* New York: Anchor Books, 1995.

Faderman, Lillian. *Odd Girls and Twilight Lovers: A History of Lesbian Life in Twentieth-Century America.* New York: Penguin, 1991.

Fireweed: A Feminist Quarterly of Writing, Politics, Art & Culture. Da Juice!: A Black Lesbian Thang (special issue). Summer, 1995.

Folisade. *Quicksand: African American Lesbian Erotica.* Palo Alto: BAP, 1992.

Gomez, Jewelle. *Forty-Three Septembers.* Ithaca, NY: Firebrand Books, 1993.

_____. *Gilda Stories.* Ithaca, NY: Firebrand Books, 1991.

Holoch, Naomi and Joan Nestle. *Women on Women 2.* New York: Plume, 1993.

Lee, C. Allyson and Makeda Silvera, eds. *Pearls of Passion: A Treasury of Lesbian Erotica.* Toronto: Sister Vision Press, 1995.

Likosky, Stephan, ed. *Coming Out: An Anthology of International Gay and Lesbian Writings.* New York: Pantheon Books, 1992.

Lorde, Audre. *A Burst of Light.* Ithaca, NY: Firebrand, 1988.

____. *Sister Outsider.* Freedom, CA: Crossing Press, 1984.

____. *Zami: A New Spelling of My Name.* Freedom, CA: Crossing Press, 1982.

Marcus, Eric. *Is It a Choice? Answers to Three Hundred of the Most Frequently Asked Questions About Gay Men and Lesbians.* San Francisco: HarperSanFrancisco, 1993.

Miller, Neil. *Out of the Past: Gay and Lesbian History from 1869 to the Present.* New York: Vintage Books, 1995.

____. *Out In the World: Gay and Lesbian Life from Buenos Aires to Bangkok.* New York: Random House, 1992.

Parker, Pat. *Movement In Black: The Collected Poetry of Pat Parker, 1961-1978.* Ithaca, NY: Firebrand Books, 1978.

Penelope, Julia and Susan J. Wolfe, eds. *The Original Coming Out Stories.* Freedom, CA: Crossing Press, 1989.

Ramos, Juanita, ed. *Compañeras: Latina Lesbians.* London: Routledge, 1994.

Roberts, J.R. *Black Lesbians: An Annotated Bibliography.*
Tallahasee, FL: Naiad Press, 1981.

Sherman, Charlotte Watson, ed. *Sisterfire: Black Womanist
Fiction and Poetry.* New York: HarperCollins, 1994.

Shockley, Ann Allen. *The Black and White of It.* Tallahassee:
Naiad Press, 1980.

Silvera, Makeda. *Her Head a Village & Other Stories.*
Vancouver: Press Gang Publishers, 1994.

Silvera, Makeda, ed. *Piece of My Heart.* Toronto: Sister Vision
Press, 1991.

Sinclair, April. *Ain't Gonna Be the Same Fool Twice.* New York:
Hyperion, 1996.

Singer, Bennett L., ed. *Growing Up Gay/Growing Up Lesbian.*
New York: New Press, 1994.

Smith, Barbara, ed. *Home Girls.* New York: Kitchen Table:
Women of Color Press, 1983.

Vida, Ginny, ed. *The New Our Right To Love.* New York:
Touchstone, 1996.

Walker, Alice. *The Color Purple.* New York: Washington
Square Press, 1982.

Youngblood, Shay. *Big Mama Stories.* Ithaca, NY: Firebrand
Books,1989.

Contributors' notes

Donna Allegra is most recently anthologized in *SportsDykes,* edited by Susan Fox Rogers; *Lesbian Erotics,* edited by Karla Jay; *All the Ways Home: Short Stories About Children and the Lesbian and Gay Community,* edited by Andy Rizzo, Jo Schneiderman, Lisa Schweig, Jan Shafer and Judith Stein; *Queer View Mirror,* edited by James C. Johnstone and Karen X. Tulchinksy; *Dyke Life: From Growing Up to Growing Old — A Celebration of the Lesbian Experience,* edited by Karla Jay; *My Lover Is a Woman — Contemporary Lesbian Love Poems,* edited by Leslea Newman; *Lesbian Short Fiction,* edited by Jinx Beers; and *Close Calls: New Lesbian Fiction,* edited by Susan Fox Rogers.

Martine C. Barbier is a 24-year-old Haitian-American graduate of Pace University in New York City with a B.A. in Human Relations/Psychology. She works extensively in the Haitian community as an advocate for the rights of immigrants, refugees and persons who are living with the HIV/AIDS virus. She also is an active member of BLAGH (Bisexual, Lesbian and Gay Haitians) and a Haitian lesbian women's discussion group, Fanm Ansanm, which means "Women Together" in Haitian Creole. "A Path to Wholeness" is her first published work and part of a novel in progress.

L.K. Barnett, graduate of the University of Missouri-Kansas City, is a 22-year-old short story writer and essayist. Currently a graduate student in the department of Women's History at Sarah Lawrence College in Bronxville, NY, she is fond of travel and is an avid jazz listener/jazz historian. L.K. has contributed to the *Harvard Gay and Lesbian Review* and more recently the ongoing anthology, *Lesbian Short Fiction,* where her short story "New Kid on the Block" and her choreopoem "Rituals" appear.

Gwendolyn Bikis is a Baltimore-bred white lesbian. A novelist and saxophonist, she teaches for the Oakland Adult Schools. Excerpts of her first novel, from which "Cleo's Gone" is derived, are also published in *Catalyst, The Persistent Desire, Sister/ Stranger* and a number of other places. She lives in Oakland, CA, where she is at work on *Cleave to Me, Mama.*

Becky Birtha is the author of two collections of short stories, *For Nights Like This One: Stories of Loving Women* (Frog in the Well, 1983) and *Lovers' Choice* (Seal, 1987) and a poetry collection entitled *The Forbidden Poems* (Seal, 1991). Her stories from *Lovers' Choice* have been anthologized in more than 20 college textbooks and trade anthologies, including *Women on Women* (New American Library, 1990), *We Are the Stories We Tell* (Pantheon, 1989), *Breaking Ice* (Viking Penguin, 1990) and *Daughters of Africa* (Pandora Press, 1991). She received an Individual Fellowship in Literature from the Pennsylvania Council on the Arts in 1985, and a Creative Writing Fellowship Grant from the National Endowment for the Arts in 1988. She lives in Philadelphia.

Sharon Bridgforth is the author of *voices in the dark*, a 76-page book of poetry and tales; *shadows ... that which is cast to the side*, an HIV education art film; *sepia's blues*, a dramatic video-tape presentation distributed by the National Black Programming Consortium; and *lovve/rituals & rage* and *no mo blues*, both poetic/drama pieces performed by Root Wy'mn Theatre Co. based in Austin, Texas. She is the artistic director of the Root Wy'mn Theatre Co.

"in my work
i'd like to
provoke dialogue/promote diversity
and urge unification amongst
people of colour

i'd like to inspect/dissect and
discuss issues that affect living-being
of Afrikan descent in patriarchal-euro-america

i'd like to take notice of
the forgotten-folk

wy'mn/children/homosexuals/the
financially disempowered

i believe
it is time we see
the us in She
the you in me
so that we can begin to be a
little kinder to each other
ourselves/the Earth
maybe then we can
dispel silence/shame
and premature dying."

Tonia Bryan is a black dyke artist, writer, poet, seamstress, hairdresser and mother of one cat from hell. Born in Barbados and indoctrinated in Canada, she spends much time exploring her/SELF and picking emotional scabs. She is one of the founding members of De Poonani Posse — a multitalented Black lesbian cultural production house — and a member of the *Fireweed* editorial collective.

Cheryl Clarke is the author of four books of poetry, *Narratives: Poems in the Tradition of Black Women, Living as a Lesbian, Humid Pitch* and *Experimental Love*. She lives and works in New Jersey. She is perpetually interested in lesbian bodies as subjects of poetry.

Tonda Clarke is a writer, activist and gay youth mentor. Her work has been published in *Focus Point, Colors* and *Lavender* magazines, and she is currently finishing a play for production. She serves on the board of the Lavender Forum in Minneapolis. She recently founded Aché, an African-American gay/lesbian/bisexual/transgender spirituality group. She is a lipstick-Libra femme, native of Chicago, and currently resides in Minneapolis.

Alexis De Veaux is a poet, short story writer, playwright, and essayist whose work is nationally and internationally known. Among her works are a memoir, *Spirits in the Street* (Doubleday,

301

1973); an award-winning children's book, *Na-Ni* (Harper & Row, 1973); *Don't Explain*, a biography of jazz great Billie Holiday (Harper & Row, 1980); *Blue Heat: A Portfolio of Poems and Drawings* (Diva Publishing Enterprises, 1985); and a second children's book, *An Enchanted Hair Tale* (Harper & Row, 1987), recipient of the 1988 Coretta Scott King Award presented by the American Library Association, and the 1991 Lorraine Hansberry Award for Excellence in African American Children's Literature. She holds a doctorate in American Studies from the State University of New York at Buffalo, where she is currently on faculty.

Gale "Sky" Edeawo is an African-American writer of poetry, prose and editorials, and has begun the challenge of writing short stories. She was most recently published in the anthology *From Wedded Wife to Lesbian Life.*

Tiffani Frazier is 24 years old and lives in Chicago.

Roxane Gay is a 20-something writer baking in the bread basket of America. She hopes to graduate before the year 2000 and works at whatever will pay the bills. She lives with her fiancée Zanna, her car Matilda, no plants or cats, and Aristotle, her larger than life teddy bear.

Lena-Nsomeka Gomes is a first-generation Cape Verde-American lesbian feminist, born and raised in Boston. She writes poetry and nonfiction, and has been published in various journals, including *Aché* magazine. She is the founder of AFROS — Association for Right On Sisters — in Boston. She has worked for eight years in the field of social work for HIV/AIDS and substance abuse; currently she is a substance abuse counselor in Oakland, CA.

Jewelle Gomez is originally from Boston and lived in New York City for 22 years, where she worked in television and theater, as well as for the State Arts Council. She was on the founding board of the Gay and Lesbian Alliance Against Defamation (GLAAD) and is a frequent contributor to lesbian publications. She currently lives in San Francisco, where she teaches creative writing. She created the script, based on her novel *The Gilda Stories*, for the dance/music/theatre production *Bones and Ash*, performed by Urban Bush Women, and is the author of a collection of essays, *Forty-three Septembers* and a third collection of poetry, *Oral Tradition*.

Imani Henry is an actor/poet/political activist. She won second place in the 1996 Outwrite National Queer Poetry Slam Championship. Her short story, "In the Air," appears in *Virgin Territory 2*; excerpts from "Bits and Pieces" will appear in an upcoming Alyson Publications book.
"— honor to be part of the book, happy to be alive, hoping to kick some ass..."

Michele Hunter was born in New York City. Her mother is French-Canadian and her father is African-American. She is an independent scholar, painter, writer and aspiring comedienne. She has an M.A. in French Literature from Harvard University.

Terri Jewell was a radical black feminist activist, poet, speaker and author. She was born in Louisville, KY, and came out in the mid-1970s in New Jersey. She was the editor of *The Black Woman's Gumbo Ya-Ya: Quotations By Black Women* and the author of a collection of poetry, *Succulent Heretic*. Her poetry and prose have appeared in numerous anthologies and periodicals, including *The Black Scholar, Women of Power, The African-American Review, Sinister Wisdom* and *Calyx*. She passed away Nov. 26, 1995 at the age of 41.

Renita Martin is a Boston-based writer/performance artist whose works have been published by Quill Books, Watermark Press, *Aché* magazine, the *Boston Globe* and several other publications. She has traveled nationally touring *Rhythm Visions Never Do Be Finished*, based on her book of poetry by the same title, and performance pieces, *Love Songs From the War* and *Peace in the Midst*.

Language, rhythms as language, language as function is my heritage. I cannot remember a time when I did not write and don't know, frankly,

how I would be in this world without language. In my world, the space of language both houses and expresses my passions. Perhaps that's why every poem I write feels like a love poem.
— renita

Hope Massiah was born in Barbados and brought up in South London, England. She has enjoyed past lives as a math teacher and an HIV educator, but in 1995 she decided to reinvent herself yet again, so she gave up her identity as a workaholic voluntary sector manager and ran away to New York with nothing but her journals, her copy of *Acts of Faith* and a burning desire to write — and two large suitcases full of carefully coordinated clothes and matching accessories. She discovered that writing makes her happy and was last seen skipping down the street, laughing at her own jokes.

Liz Messerly was born in 1967, raised in Iowa, and now resides in Washington, DC. She also writes poetry; this is her first publication. At present, she works on Capitol Hill for Sen. Tom Harkin, a staunch Democrat from her home state.

mistinguette is a poet, writer and AIDS service worker. Her poetry and short fiction have appeared in *Common Lives/Lesbian Lives, Sparking: An Ohio Wimmins Anthology*, and the script of *Natural Boundaries: Poems of Exploration and Imagination*. She is living happily ever after in Cleveland, Ohio, and is always disappointed that she has no one left to come out to on National Coming Out Day.

Denise Moore is "the fairest of the them all," a high-yellow writer currently residing in New Orleans, LA. She is the author of *American Woman*, a book of poetry featuring "The Black Diva," and edited *Narcissus Unbound*, an anthology of erotica by women who work in the sex industry. She recently completed her first screenplay.

Letta Neely is the author of two chapbooks: *gawd and alluh huh sistahs* and *when we were mud*. Originally from Indianapolis, IN, she now lives in Harlem.

Ekua Omosupe lives in Aptos, CA. She teaches writing, women's studies and critical thinking at Cabrillo College. She is mother of three children and has three grandchildren. Ekua and her partner, Maria Davila, co-own a business: MAKUA PRO-DUCTIONS, ethnic arts, crafts and jewelry. She is current poetry editor of *Sinister Wisdom*. Ekua's poems and essays are published in various journals and anthologies; her most recent contribution is to a new anthology, *Quarry West Magazine*, to be published March 1997 by University of California at Santa Cruz.

Kimberly "Q" Purnell is a lesbian actress who is waiting to be discovered. She has been called "the Josephine Baker of this century" and looks forward to one day performing in a show where the actress that's playing the lesbian really is one! She enjoys writing articles that are controversial, and proving the heterosexual community wrong by being a "femme fatale" instead of what they think a lesbian is supposed to look like. She has much support and love from her family, friends, her one and only child (Vamp, her cat) and love of her life, Diane.

Mattie Richardson was born and raised in New York of African-American and Caribbean heritage. Her fiction, essays and poetry can be found in various anthologies and journals. Mattie is an activist as well as a writer. Currently, she is working with lesbian, bisexual and gay teenagers and helping to raise awareness of lesbian and gay issues in the public schools of rural Vermont and New Hampshire.

Brigitte M. Roberts is an African-American lesbian writer who was born and raised in Brooklyn, NY. She is a social worker, publisher, producer and activist. Her work has appeared in *The Brooklyn Trend* and the chapbook titled *In the Spirit of Affirmation*. She currently resides in Oakland, CA.

Makeda Silvera lives in Toronto, Canada. She is the author and anthologizer of several books which include: *Silenced, Growing Up Black, Remembering G and other stories, Her Head a Village and other stories, Piece of My Heart: A Lesbian of Colour*

Anthology, The Other Woman: Women of Colour in Contempo-
rary Canadian Literature and *Pearls of Passion: A Treasury of*
Lesbian Erotica.

Sheree Slaughter is a 40-year-old African-American, a proud
lesbian for 25 years and an established poet. She enjoys writing
serious as well as humorous poems for and about women. Her
favorite hobbies include weight-lifting, bowling, tennis and
eating. She's in love with a very beautiful young lady and has a
black cat named Midnight. Her poems have been published in
*The Chicago Defender, Outlines, Aché, Planet Roc Alternative
Arts Journal, Les Talk Magazine*, and *Lavender Life Magazine.*

sherece taffe created sharmylae, co-founded De Poonani Posse
and BLACKberry and practices S/M to fill her spiritual, political, emotional and sexual needs. she aspires to nurture the loving
relationship actualized recently when she fell in love — with
herself! her desire to survive intersects with her need to write
and her delusions of grandeur!

Karen Thompson is a 25-year-old doctoral candidate in performance studies at NYU. She is first-generation American from a
religious, maroon-descended Jamaican mother. "Q & A" was one
of the first poems she ever wrote. Now there's more! Write for a
catalogue!

Nailah Taliba Tulinegwe is a native D.C. womon, educated in
D.C. public schools, has interests in writing, journalism, HIV/
AIDS awareness discussions. Named Nailah (one who succeeds)
due to difficult period in life; with Faith in Creator, knew I'd
overcome adversity successfully. All lessons (though some are
unpleasant) are for my learning, no negatives. "Seek empowerment to empower others..."

Laura Irene Wayne is an African-American lesbian painter,
printmaker, poet, graphic artist and writer. For the past 14 years
she has exhibited locally, nationally and internationally. Her
work has appeared in and on the covers of various magazines,
books, journals and newspapers, and can be found in many

private collections. She owns and operates Womyn Work: a fine
art company in Sacramento, CA, featuring womyn-identified
paintings, prints, poetry, T-shirts and greeting cards. Laura's
artwork and poetry reflect the heritage, culture and experience of
her people and their environment. Some of the images she
creates are portrayed with no facial features to avoid perpetuat-
ing stereotypes and to cultivate sisterhood.

Liza Wesley is a pseudonym for a woman of 38. She lives in the
Washington area. Liza works in an office by day and writes when
she can.

Michelle Wilkinson finds joy in Atlanta, GA, feeding people
ideas, food and perspective.

Arlene Williams is a Black Indigenous Lesbian Active Feminist
Revolutionary Poet Student of life. I was given life in Atlantic
City, NJ, and I now live in Pleasantville, NJ. At 20 years of age, I
am working to publish a collection of my words. I do this with
hopes to break many silences. In my growth I struggle, so now I
make the personal political for a better existence.

Shilanda Woolridge is a 22-year-old creole gal born in Louisiana and raised between here and there as a nomadic Air Force
brat. Currently a creative advertising senior at the University of
Texas at Austin nursing some baby dreads.

Eva Yaa Asantewaa is a native New Yorker of Caribbean
heritage. A former dance critic for *The Village Voice, Dance
Magazine,* and other publications, she currently writes reviews
for the *Dance Online* web site. She was most recently published
in *The Zenith of Desire: Contemporary Lesbian Poems About
Sex, Queer Dog: Homo Pup Poetry,* and *Kuumba* (Summer
1997). Her work will also appear in the upcoming *Other Coun-
tries: Black Gay and Lesbian Voices Rising.*

Shay Youngblood is the author of *The Big Mama Stories,* a
collection of short fiction; stage plays *Shakin' the Mess Out of
Misery, Talking Bones* and *Black Power Barbie,* and a novel,

Soul Kiss.

akhaji zakiya is a Toronto-based air gemini who enjoys riding language to convey meaning and ideas. She is currently chilling in sub/urban terrain, contemplating methods of generating resources without selling her stuff during this precarious era of "global economic restructuring." Otherwise she can be found spending large amounts of time talking, looking for the sun to bask in and avoiding drama while trying to harness the "power of the erotic."

Permissions

312

Here's what the critics are saying about
does your mama know?

"These voices are varied as are the tales they tell. Haitian, Jamerican, Afro-Canadian, biracial, Southern U.S., London by way of Barbados. Ages 14 to 90. ... It is extremely rare to see a book of any kind that reflects the diversity of black people in North America, not only economically, but ethnically."
— R. Erica Doyle, *Women in the Life Magazine*

"Without discounting differences in the lesbian community, it is nevertheless heartening to find commonality in so central an experience as our discovery of ourselves."
— Deborah Peifer, *The Bay Guardian*

"Moore has collected well. The black lesbian voice is missing from this country's gay literary insurgence no longer."
— Emma Hayes, *HX for Her*

"Moore does the community a service by not censoring her anthology, by allowing black lesbian voices to be heard in rich and varied ways. Voices that are angry, empowered, naive, streetwise, urban, suburban, and erotic."
— Barbara I. Bond, *Lambda Book Report*

"Few such voices have been raised to sing the history of African American lesbians. Editor Lisa C. Moore noticed that and has set about to correct the omission, and she has done a masterful job of it."
—Dale Edwyna Smith, *Lesbian Review of Books*

ORDER FORM

To order single copies, send a check or money order for
$19.95 per book plus $3 shipping to:

RedBone Press
P.O. Box 1805
Austin, TX 78767

Name:

Address:

City: State: Zip:

Telephone: (   )

DISTRIBUTED TO THE BOOK TRADE BY:

LPC Group
1436 West Randolph St.
Chicago, IL 60607
(800) 626-4330